Two Plus Two Is Not Five

Easy Methods to Learn Addition + Subtraction

Susan Greenwald, M.A. Ed.

LP **LONGEVITY PUBLISHING, LLC**
Englewood, Colorado • www.longevitypublishing.com

This book has been a labor of love
for students of all ages,
and will continue to be beneficial
for as long as children need to memorize math facts.

For Madison Olivia, with love.

Two Plus Two Is Not Five:
Easy Methods to Learn Addition and Subtraction
LP 200
This book is an Evvy Award winner.

Longevity Publishing LLC
Englewood, Colorado
www.longevitypublishing.com
ISBN 13: 978-0-9777323-0-2
10 9 8 7 6 5

First printing 2006
Second printing 2007
Third printing 2009
Fourth printing 2010

Edited by: Ellen Raymond

*With the permission of Teacher Created Resources, some trick names and concepts are used in this
book that have appeared previously in* **How to Teach Math Facts** *by Susan Greenwald.*

Table of Contents

Tier Instructions and Information pages precede the beginning of each tier.
Be sure to read the Tier Instructions and Information pages before assigning worksheets!

Answers are provided on the reverse side of the Tier Instructions and Information pages.

Introduction

Two Plus Two Is Not Five, Easy Methods to Learn Addition and Subtraction, is a practical, supplementary workbook to teach the addition and subtraction facts to students, and includes tricks from my first book, *How to Teach Math Facts,* published in 1999 by Teacher Created Resources. The purpose of both books is to help students memorize the math facts. *Two Plus Two Is Not Five* introduces the addition and subtraction facts with many easy-to-learn tricks and provides extensive practice opportunities, because mastery of basic math facts is essential for success in computation skills and solving word problems.

The math tricks and their respective practice pages are arranged in a format that is useful to ★ parents, ★ classroom teachers, ★ home schooling educators, ★ resource room teachers, and ★ tutors.

Teachers and parents will find that this is suitable for learners of any age who need to master the basic addition and subtraction facts. For this reason, the workbook pages were intentionally not designed for a particular grade level.

> **The 232 reproducible practice pages will appeal to:**
> - Beginners
> - Elementary school children needing instruction, practice, or review of the math facts
> - Children in remedial programs
> - Children in accelerated programs who need to memorize math facts
> - Children with math disabilities
> - Older students who still struggle because they just never memorized the math facts

Parents and teachers will appreciate how easy it is to facilitate the learning process for children.

- Self-explanatory pages are straightforward to administer.

- Lessons can be easily individualized for different learning abilities.

- Most of the pages are divided into two sections so that half sheets can be easily assigned. This will be beneficial for very young learners or those intimidated by a whole page of math to do!

- Math fact cards are assigned to go along with the practice pages.

- Children will remember answers to the addition and subtraction facts because they are learning the tricks, doing written math practice, and reviewing with the math fact cards.

- Math assignments will be completed with confidence and children will enjoy their success.

How to Use This Book

Before assigning pages from the workbook, refer to the **Tier Instructions and Information** page preceding the beginning of each tier.

For use with individuals needing review or remedial work:

Baseline Known Facts

1. Use a set of addition and a set of subtraction cards to test the child to determine the **Baseline** of which facts are known.

   Excluding the <u>Zero</u> facts, there are 81 addition and 81 subtraction facts to be mastered.

Record Known Facts

2. **Known** facts are those addition and subtraction facts that are answered quickly and correctly. Children should not count to get an answer.

   Record those known facts on the **Math Facts Baseline Recorder** provided on page 235. Then transfer the information to the **Record-Keeping Checklist** on page 234 where empty spaces allow you to see easily which facts in each tier need to be learned.

Use Counters

3. Use counting items such as cubes, buttons, crayons, or paper clips for the initial introduction of the math fact with its trick.

   Children need to demonstrate understanding of the meaning of addition and subtraction.

Record Progress

4. As new facts are introduced, be sure to fill in the boxes on the **Record-Keeping Checklist.** Seeing those filled-in spaces will give children a feeling of accomplishment!

The Pace

5. Practice should be scheduled at least three times per week.

   The workbook includes 56 sets of introductions and was designed to introduce a new trick or set of facts on each lesson day, but this does not necessarily mean every day.

   The pace should be set by the child's ability. Not all children will be ready to advance at the same rate. Some will be able to handle one set of new facts in a day; others may need more time. Children in accelerated programs could be introduced to new facts at a faster pace.

   As math facts are mastered, teachers can integrate them into the rest of the math curriculum.

Math Fact Cards

6. The math fact cards to be assigned are listed on the **Tier Instructions and Information** page preceding the beginning of each tier. As each set of math facts is introduced, use 3" by 5" blank index cards to make math fact cards.

Parents are encouraged to provide daily practice at home with a set of math fact cards.

Teachers working 1:1 with children can incorporate practice of the math fact cards into their daily program.

Assign Pages

7. Following the introductory practice page for the new facts, allow the children to complete the practice pages. These pages provide application and review between the introductions of new facts.

Teachers can assign these practice pages for class work and/or homework.

Children should complete at least part if not all of each of the **Cumulative Practice** and **Tier Review** pages. This ensures that they will not forget previously taught facts.

Use Trick Names

8. Encourage use of the trick name.

It is important for children to associate a fact with a trick rather than count out an answer on fingers.

When stuck on a math fact, they should be reminded to think of the trick and state the trick name to recall the answer.

Extra Practice

9. Tricks are reviewed throughout the book by themselves or in a variety of combinations.

Children who are having difficulty learning a trick can be reassigned pages that offer practice for that trick. Refer to the **Index** for those page numbers.

Answers

10. Answers are provided on the reverse side of the **Tier Instructions and Information** pages.

11. A Certificate for Mastery is provided on page 233.

For use with beginners who need to learn all of the addition and subtraction facts:
Start with Tier 1 and follow steps 3 through 8.

For use with a whole class of students who already know some math facts:
Begin with Tier 1 and decide which facts need to be taught by looking at the **Record-Keeping Checklist.** Follow steps 3 through 8. Set the pace according to your class and, if at all possible, divide the class into smaller groups to provide some individualization.

Types of Workbook Pages

Each of the six tiers can be easily identified by the edge of the paper. After the math facts are introduced, Tier 1 math facts will be reviewed throughout Tier 1. The five other tiers review all the math facts from previous tiers.

There are four basic types of practice. Not all children will need to complete each page in its entirety. Most of the practice pages are divided into a top and bottom section so that shorter half-page tasks can easily be given.

Trick Introduction

These sections use a trick to teach the new math facts and may include a few facts from a previous tier. After an initial explanation, all children needing to learn the facts should complete this type of practice page.

Practice

These pages include the newly taught math facts and/or a mixture of these newest math facts along with those from one or more other tricks from a previous tier. Most children will need to do all of these pages, while others need only complete parts of them. These practice pages are perfect for reassignment when a student is having difficulty learning a trick.

Cumulative Practice

This type of practice page may follow the introduction and practice pages of each trick. The children will be checked on the newly learned trick and most of the math facts and tricks that have been taught from previous tiers. All children should complete these workbook pages, which are offered periodically throughout the book.

Tier Review

The Tier Review pages are presented at the ends of Tiers 2 through 5. Tier Review practice pages offer a lot of review of all the tricks and math facts taught in each of the respective tiers as well as the previous tiers. Most children will need to do all of these pages, while others need only complete some of them to demonstrate mastery. These pages are perfect for reassignment when a child is having difficulty learning a trick.

For children needing extra practice, just refer to the **Index** to find and assign pages that review previously taught tricks.

Sequence Within a Tier

The **Tier Instructions and Information** pages have specific instructions that need to be followed for each tier. There will also be a list of the tricks, their page numbers, and the math fact cards to be assigned with them. **The math fact cards should be practiced on a daily basis.**

The organization of the workbook offers a nontraditional, flexible sequence.

- The six tiers need to be completed in sequence, but each tier following Tier 1 allows for flexibility within itself.

- Within each of Tiers 2 through 5, you may pick which trick introduction to start with. You may choose to teach the last trick in the tier before you teach the first one.

- Exceptions are noted in bold on the **Tier Instructions and Information** pages. Generally, when more than one set of math facts of the same trick is introduced within a tier, then assign those facts in the order they are presented, but it is not necessary to teach the second set of the same trick immediately following the first.

> All the facts from **Tier 1** are continuously reviewed throughout **Tier 2**.
> New tricks in **Tier 2** are reviewed at the end of **Tier 2**.

> All the facts from **Tiers 1** and **2** are continuously reviewed throughout **Tier 3**.
> New tricks in **Tier 3** are reviewed at the end of **Tier 3**.

> All the facts from **Tiers 1, 2,** and **3** are continuously reviewed throughout **Tier 4**.
> New tricks in **Tier 4** are reviewed at the end of **Tier 4**.

> All the facts from **Tiers 1, 2, 3,** and **4** are continuously reviewed throughout **Tier 5**.
> New tricks in **Tier 5** are reviewed at the end of **Tier 5**.

> All the facts from **Tiers 1, 2, 3, 4,** and **5** are continuously reviewed throughout **Tier 6**.
> New tricks in **Tier 6** are reviewed at the end of **Tier 6**.

Tier 1

Instructions and Information

Follow the given sequence.

All the facts are continuously reviewed as the new ones are taught.

It is not necessary to assign all 18 of the **Zero** facts.

Page	Trick	Math fact cards to be assigned:
1-2	**Number +1**	1+1, 2+1, 3+1, 4+1, 5+1, 6+1, 7+1, 8+1, 9+1, 1+2, 1+3, 1+4, 1+5, 1+6, 1+7, 1+8, 1+9
3-4	**Doubles**	2+2, 5+5
5-7	**Backwards 1**	10-1, 9-1, 8-1, 7-1, 6-1, 5-1, 4-1, 3-1, 2-1
8-9	**Doubles**	3+3
10-11	**Zero** (Number + Zero) (Zero + Number)	1+0, 2+0, 3+0, 4+0, 5+0, 6+0, 7+0, 8+0, 9+0 0+1, 0+2, 0+3, 0+4, 0+5, 0+6, 0+7, 0+8, 0+9
12-13	**Doubles**	4+4
14-16	**Doubles Subtraction**	4-2, 10-5
17-19	**Right Next to Each Other**	10-9, 9-8, 8-7, 7-6, 6-5, 5-4, 4-3, 3-2
20-21	**Doubles Subtraction**	6-3, 8-4
22-24	**2 Ladder**	2+4, 4+2, 2+6, 6+2, 2+8, 8+2

Tier 1 Answers

Page 1
2,4,6,8,10
5,8,3,9,7
10,6,7,5,4
4,8,10,5,7,2
9,6,7,4,10,6,8

Page 2
2,3,4,7,6,9
5,8,10,3,5,6
3,3,5,5,7,8,10
10,4,6,9,7,8,4
5,8,10,3,9,6,2

Page 3
4,2,10,4,10,2,10
4,9,10,8,3,7,5
6,4,10,2,4,4,10
3,8,9,10,4,10,7
10,5,4,4,10,9,2
4,9,10,10,3,8,6

Page 4
4,7,6,10
9,10,4,8
10,5,3,10
8,4,9,6
10,7,3,4
2,10,4,5
10,5,9,4,7,10,6
4,4,8,5,10,2,3

Page 5
9,6,4,8,3,7,5,2,1
9,7,5,4,8,3
6,8,9,3,6,1,7
9,2,8,5
7,6,4,1
3,9,5,7
8,4,3,2

Page 6
6,9,5,3,2,8,4
7,4,10,10,8,5,3
6,9,1,4,10,9,4
8,10,4,5,6,7,4

Page 7
8,6,9,3,5,1,4
8,10,3,7,9,5,7
4,9,2,2,3,6,4
7,1,4,8,4,10,5
3,6,2,9,9,5,7
4,7,3,4,10,9,6
10,8,10,7,8,4,1

Page 8
6,4,6,10,4,6,2
10,6,2,6,10,4,6
8,3,6,5
6,4,9,2
10,8,3,6
6,10,5,6
7,4,6,4
8,5,9,4
7,3,1,6

Page 9
10,6,2,4,5,9,7
4,8,5,6,9,4,8
10,6,2,10,7,10,6
10,6,4,3
8,8,4,6
9,10,5,1
6,9,6,10
2,10,6,6
7,6,10,6

Page 10
3,4,8
6,5,7
1,8,6,4,4,9,2
6,10,3,5,2,10,6
3,3,8,4,2,6,10
6,7,1,5,4,2,9

Page 11
5,3,8,5,9,9,4
1,7,6,5,10,6,4
2,4,7,2,6,3,8
5,9,1,2,8,2,7
6,8,6,10,2,8,10
3,6,6,4,3,6,4
5,4,6,9,1,7,8
4,8,7,4,10,9,5

Page 12
8,6,8,10,4,8,2
4,10,6,8,2,4,8
6,8,4,2,10,8,6
8,10,8,6,5,4,8
2,1,7,4,6,8,3
9,4,8,6,10,2,8

Page 13
10,6,2,9,2,8,1
4,5,8,10,6,8,4
7,2,6,3,8,4,4
6,8,2,1,3,5,10
9,2,8,10,8,6,4
6,3,7,8,5,8,7
8,7,1,5,4,6,4
7,3,9,8,2,9,5

Page 14
10,4,2,5,2,2,5
5,2,2,10,5,5,2
10,6,5,4,2,2,10
2,5,6,5,2,8,2

Page 15
8,3,5,5,2,7,2
6,2,10,9,6,5,10
8,5,4,2,3,6,8
10,9,10,5,8,5,8
6,2,7,2,6,4,4
10,4,7,3,5,9,9
6,2,5,9,7,7,6
4,8,1,8,3,5,2

Page 16
9,5,4,6,8,6,2
8,9,2,10,6,1,3
9,4,5,2,5,7,8
2,5,1,2,6,5,7
2,2,8,5
9,3,6,7
3,10,8,8
7,4,6,9
3,5,2,10

Page 17
))) \ )
))) \ \ \ )
\ )) \ )))
All = 1

Page 18
1 1 1 \
1 1 \ 1 1 \ 1
1 1 1 \ 1 1 1
1,1,3,7,1,6,4
9,1,8,3,9,5,1
2,1,6,7,1,5,1
8,1,5,1,9,10,1

Page 19
1,1,7,1,6,10,4
2,8,1,1,3,5,2
1,9,6,1,1,2,1
4,5,1,8,1,2,8
1,4,6,6
1,10,1,5
1,1,6,1
6,7,1,2
5,3,1,8

Page 20
6,3,3,3,8,4,4
3,8,4,4,3,3,4
4,3,4,5,3,2,4
3,1,1,2,4,5,1
1,4,2,1,3,1,4
4,1,3,10,4,3,4

Page 21
4,5,5,8,6,5,7
6,2,1,1,3,8,10
3,1,6,3,9,8,1
2,9,1,3,4,6,4
2,3,3,7
1,4,10,4
8,1,1,9
10,6,4,3
1,5,5,5

Page 22
10,6
4,8,6,10
2,8,10,4,6,8
4,6,8,10,8,6,10
8,8,6,6,10,10,8

Page 23
10,8,6,2,2,8,6
6,3,10,10,8,6,10
8,6,10,2,8,3,4
6,10,8,8,4,5,8
8,10,4,5,7,5,6
10,8,7,3,8,8,6
9,6,9,2,6,10,8
4,1,8,3,10,10,6

Page 24
10,1,6,1,1,8,10
1,6,1,1,10,6,8
8,1,10,6,1,8,1
10,1,8,7,6,8,5
10,10,6,4,4,2,3
7,6,1,10,4,1,5
8,5,3,6,10,6,1
5,8,1,7,6,9,8

Name _____

TRICK Number +1

Can you count to 10?

Tell what comes next.

1,____	3,____	5,____	7,____	9,____
4,____	7,____	2,____	8,____	6,____
9,____	5,____	6,____	4,____	3,____

What is one more? Write the greater number.

3						
2	3	7	9	4	6	1

8	5	6	3	9	5	7

Go up like an elevator.

9+1= **10**

8+1= **9**

7+1= **8**

6+1= **7**

5+1= **6**

4+1= **5**

3+1= **4**

2+1= **3**

1+1= **2**

1

Name _____

Try **Number +1**.

1 + 1	2 + 1	3 + 1	6 + 1	5 + 1	8 + 1

4 + 1	7 + 1	9 + 1	2 + 1	4 + 1	5 + 1

LOOK. These are the same.

$$
\begin{array}{cc} 3 \\ + 1 \\ \hline 4 \end{array} \qquad
\begin{array}{cc} 1 \\ + 3 \\ \hline 4 \end{array} \qquad
\begin{array}{cc} 6 \\ + 1 \\ \hline 7 \end{array} \qquad
\begin{array}{cc} 1 \\ + 6 \\ \hline 7 \end{array}
$$

Practice **Number +1**.

2 + 1	1 + 2	4 + 1	1 + 4	6 + 1	1 + 7	1 + 9

9 + 1	3 + 1	1 + 5	1 + 8	1 + 6	7 + 1	1 + 3

1 + 4	7 + 1	1 + 9	2 + 1	8 + 1	5 + 1	1 + 1

Name _____

TRICK <u>Doubles</u>

Learn   2   1 2
            + 2
            ———   3 4
            4

5 fingers
+ 5 fingers
10 fingers

Practice **<u>Doubles</u>** and **<u>Number +1</u>**.

2	1	5	2	5	1	5
+ 2	+ 1	+ 5	+ 2	+ 5	+ 1	+ 5

2	1	5	7	2	1	1
+ 2	+ 8	+ 5	+ 1	+ 1	+ 6	+ 4

5	3	9	1	1	2	5
+ 1	+ 1	+ 1	+ 1	+ 3	+ 2	+ 5

1	1	8	5	2	1	6
+ 2	+ 7	+ 1	+ 5	+ 2	+ 9	+ 1

5	4	2	3	5	1	1
+ 5	+ 1	+ 2	+ 1	+ 5	+ 8	+ 1

2	1	9	5	2	7	1
+ 2	+ 8	+ 1	+ 5	+ 1	+ 1	+ 5

Two Plus Two Is Not Five, Easy Methods To Learn Addition and Subtraction **3**

Name _____

LOOK. These are the same.

$$\begin{array}{r} 5 \\ + 5 \\ \hline 10 \end{array} \qquad 5+5= 10 \qquad\qquad \begin{array}{r} 2 \\ + 2 \\ \hline 4 \end{array} \qquad 2+2= 4$$

2+2= _____	6+1= _____	5+1= _____	9+1= _____
1+8= _____	5+5= _____	3+1= _____	1+7= _____
1+9= _____	4+1= _____	1+2= _____	5+5= _____
7+1= _____	2+2= _____	8+1= _____	1+5= _____
5+5= _____	1+6= _____	2+1= _____	2+2= _____
1+1= _____	5+5= _____	1+3= _____	1+4= _____

Practice **Doubles** and **Number +1**.

$$\begin{array}{r} 5 \\ +5 \\ \hline \end{array} \quad \begin{array}{r} 1 \\ +4 \\ \hline \end{array} \quad \begin{array}{r} 8 \\ +1 \\ \hline \end{array} \quad \begin{array}{r} 2 \\ +2 \\ \hline \end{array} \quad \begin{array}{r} 6 \\ +1 \\ \hline \end{array} \quad \begin{array}{r} 1 \\ +9 \\ \hline \end{array} \quad \begin{array}{r} 1 \\ +5 \\ \hline \end{array}$$

$$\begin{array}{r} 2 \\ +2 \\ \hline \end{array} \quad \begin{array}{r} 3 \\ +1 \\ \hline \end{array} \quad \begin{array}{r} 1 \\ +7 \\ \hline \end{array} \quad \begin{array}{r} 1 \\ +4 \\ \hline \end{array} \quad \begin{array}{r} 5 \\ +5 \\ \hline \end{array} \quad \begin{array}{r} 1 \\ +1 \\ \hline \end{array} \quad \begin{array}{r} 2 \\ +1 \\ \hline \end{array}$$

Name _____

TRICK Backwards 1

Count Backwards.

| 10 | 7 | 5 | 9 | 4 | 8 | 6 | 3 | 2 |

____ ____ ____ ____ ____ ____ ____ ____ ____

Write the number that is one less.

| **3** | **10** | **8** | **6** | **5** | **9** | **4** |
| 2 | | | | | | |

| **7** | **9** | **10** | **4** | **7** | **2** | **8** |
| | | | | | | |

What comes before?

_____ 10   _____ 3   _____ 9   _____ 6

_____ 8   _____ 7   _____ 5   _____ 2

_____ 4   _____ 10   _____ 6   _____ 8

_____ 9   _____ 5   _____ 4   _____ 3

Two Plus Two Is Not Five, Easy Methods To Learn Addition and Subtraction **5**

Name _____

Backwards 1   −1

You have 3 candy bars.

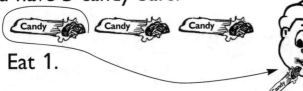

Eat 1.

$$\begin{array}{r} 3 \\ -1 \\ \hline \boxed{2} \end{array}$$

2 are left.

You have 7 candy bars.

Eat 1.

$$\begin{array}{r} 7 \\ -1 \\ \hline \boxed{6} \end{array}$$ are left.

You have 5 candy bars.

Eat 1.

$$\begin{array}{r} 5 \\ -1 \\ \hline \boxed{4} \end{array}$$ are left.

You have 10 candy bars.

Eat 1.

$$\begin{array}{r} 10 \\ -1 \\ \hline \boxed{9} \end{array}$$ are left.

Try.

$$\begin{array}{r} 7 \\ -1 \\ \hline \end{array} \qquad \begin{array}{r} 10 \\ -1 \\ \hline \end{array} \qquad \begin{array}{r} 6 \\ -1 \\ \hline \end{array} \qquad \begin{array}{r} 4 \\ -1 \\ \hline \end{array} \qquad \begin{array}{r} 3 \\ -1 \\ \hline \end{array} \qquad \begin{array}{r} 9 \\ -1 \\ \hline \end{array} \qquad \begin{array}{r} 5 \\ -1 \\ \hline \end{array}$$

Practice **Backwards 1**, **Doubles**, and **Number +1**.

$$\begin{array}{r} 8 \\ -1 \\ \hline \end{array} \qquad \begin{array}{r} 2 \\ +2 \\ \hline \end{array} \qquad \begin{array}{r} 5 \\ +5 \\ \hline \end{array} \qquad \begin{array}{r} 1 \\ +9 \\ \hline \end{array} \qquad \begin{array}{r} 1 \\ +7 \\ \hline \end{array} \qquad \begin{array}{r} 6 \\ -1 \\ \hline \end{array} \qquad \begin{array}{r} 4 \\ -1 \\ \hline \end{array}$$

$$\begin{array}{r} 5 \\ +1 \\ \hline \end{array} \qquad \begin{array}{r} 10 \\ -1 \\ \hline \end{array} \qquad \begin{array}{r} 2 \\ -1 \\ \hline \end{array} \qquad \begin{array}{r} 2 \\ +2 \\ \hline \end{array} \qquad \begin{array}{r} 5 \\ +5 \\ \hline \end{array} \qquad \begin{array}{r} 8 \\ +1 \\ \hline \end{array} \qquad \begin{array}{r} 1 \\ +3 \\ \hline \end{array}$$

$$\begin{array}{r} 9 \\ -1 \\ \hline \end{array} \qquad \begin{array}{r} 5 \\ +5 \\ \hline \end{array} \qquad \begin{array}{r} 5 \\ -1 \\ \hline \end{array} \qquad \begin{array}{r} 4 \\ +1 \\ \hline \end{array} \qquad \begin{array}{r} 7 \\ -1 \\ \hline \end{array} \qquad \begin{array}{r} 1 \\ +6 \\ \hline \end{array} \qquad \begin{array}{r} 2 \\ +2 \\ \hline \end{array}$$

Name _____

Practice **Backwards 1** and **Number +1**.

9	1	10	2	6	2	5
-1	$+5$	-1	$+1$	-1	-1	-1

7	1	4	6	8	1	8
$+1$	$+9$	-1	$+1$	$+1$	$+4$	-1

3	1	1	3	1	7	1
$+1$	$+8$	$+1$	-1	$+2$	-1	$+3$

1	2	5	1	3	9	4
$+6$	-1	-1	$+7$	$+1$	$+1$	$+1$

4	5	3	8	10	6	1
-1	$+1$	-1	$+1$	-1	-1	$+6$

Practice all tricks.

2	6	4	1	5	10	7
$+2$	$+1$	-1	$+3$	$+5$	-1	-1

1	9	5	8	7	2	2
$+9$	-1	$+5$	-1	$+1$	$+2$	-1

Two Plus Two Is Not Five, Easy Methods To Learn Addition and Subtraction   **7**

TIER I

Name _____

TRICK Doubles

Learn   3 + 3 =   6.
⬜⬜⬜   ⬜⬜⬜   ⬜⬜⬜⬜⬜⬜

3	2	3	5	2	3	1
+ 3	+ 2	+ 3	+ 5	+ 2	+ 3	+ 1

5	3	1	3	5	2	3
+ 5	+ 3	+ 1	+ 3	+ 5	+ 2	+ 3

Practice addition.

7+1= _____   2+1= _____   3+3= _____   1+4= _____

3+3= _____   3+1= _____   8+1= _____   1+1= _____

9+1= _____   1+7= _____   1+2= _____   3+3= _____

3+3= _____   5+5= _____   4+1= _____   5+1= _____

1+6= _____   2+2= _____   3+3= _____   1+3= _____

Practice subtraction.

9–1= _____   6–1= _____   10–1= _____   5–1= _____

8–1= _____   4–1= _____   2–1= _____   7–1= _____

Name _____

Practice **Doubles**, **Number +1**, and **Backwards 1**.

Watch **+** and **−**

$$
\begin{array}{ccccccc}
5 & 3 & 1 & 2 & 1 & 8 & 1 \\
+5 & +3 & +1 & +2 & +4 & +1 & +6 \\
\end{array}
$$

$$
\begin{array}{ccccccc}
1 & 9 & 6 & 3 & 10 & 2 & 7 \\
+3 & -1 & -1 & +3 & -1 & +2 & +1 \\
\end{array}
$$

$$
\begin{array}{ccccccc}
1 & 3 & 3 & 5 & 8 & 5 & 3 \\
+9 & +3 & -1 & +5 & -1 & +5 & +3 \\
\end{array}
$$

Try this way.

5+5 = _____	3+3 = _____	2+2 = _____	2+1 = _____
9−1 = _____	1+7 = _____	5−1 = _____	3+3 = _____
1+8 = _____	9+1 = _____	4+1 = _____	2−1 = _____
3+3 = _____	10−1 = _____	1+5 = _____	5+5 = _____
3−1 = _____	1+9 = _____	3+3 = _____	7−1 = _____
6+1 = _____	3+3 = _____	5+5 = _____	3+3 = _____

Two Plus Two Is Not Five, Easy Methods To Learn Addition and Subtraction **9**

Name _____

TRICK Learn <u>Zero</u>.

1 candy bar + hand none

1 candy bar + 0 more is still

 2 candy bars + 0 more is still

3 + 0 = ____   4 + 0 = ____   8 + 0 = ____

6 + 0 = ____   5 + 0 = ____   7 + 0 = ____

Practice **Zero** and **Doubles**.

1	8	3	4	2	9	2
+ 0	+ 0	+ 3	+ 0	+ 2	+ 0	+ 0

6	5	3	5	1	5	3
+ 0	+ 5	+ 0	+ 0	+ 1	+ 5	+ 3

LOOK. These are the same.

```
 2        0
+ 0      + 2
 2        2
```

3	0	8	0	1	6	5
+ 0	+ 3	+ 0	+ 4	+ 1	+ 0	+ 5

0	7	1	0	2	2	0
+ 6	+ 0	+ 0	+ 5	+ 2	+ 0	+ 9

Name _____

Practice **Number +1** and **Backwards 1**.

4 + 1	1 + 2	9 − 1	6 − 1	1 + 8	10 − 1	1 + 3
2 − 1	8 − 1	1 + 5	1 + 4	9 + 1	7 − 1	5 − 1
1 + 1	3 + 1	1 + 6	3 − 1	5 + 1	4 − 1	7 + 1

Practice all tricks. (Circle) **Zero**.

0 + 5	10 − 1	2 − 1	2 + 0	7 + 1	3 − 1	8 − 1
3 + 3	9 − 1	0 + 6	5 + 5	1 + 1	8 + 0	1 + 9
0 + 3	1 + 5	7 − 1	4 + 0	4 − 1	3 + 3	1 + 3
4 + 1	2 + 2	3 + 3	8 + 1	0 + 1	7 + 0	1 + 7
5 − 1	0 + 8	6 + 1	2 + 2	5 + 5	0 + 9	6 − 1

Two Plus Two Is Not Five, Easy Methods To Learn Addition and Subtraction 11

Name _____

TRICK Doubles

Learn

$$\begin{array}{r} 4 \\ + 4 \\ \hline 8 \end{array}$$

1 2 3 4
5 6 7 8

Practice **Doubles**.

4 + 4	3 + 3	4 + 4	5 + 5	2 + 2	4 + 4	1 + 1
2 + 2	5 + 5	3 + 3	4 + 4	1 + 1	2 + 2	4 + 4
3 + 3	4 + 4	2 + 2	1 + 1	5 + 5	4 + 4	3 + 3

Practice **Doubles** and **Backwards 1**.

4 + 4	5 + 5	4 + 4	3 + 3	6 − 1	2 + 2	9 − 1
1 + 1	2 − 1	8 − 1	5 − 1	3 + 3	4 + 4	4 − 1
10 − 1	2 + 2	4 + 4	7 − 1	5 + 5	3 − 1	4 + 4

Two Plus Two Is Not Five, Easy Methods To Learn Addition and Subtraction

Name _____

Practice **Doubles** and **Zero**.

5 + 5	3 + 3	2 + 0	9 + 0	1 + 1	4 + 4	0 + 1
0 + 4	0 + 5	4 + 4	5 + 5	6 + 0	0 + 8	2 + 2
0 + 7	1 + 1	3 + 3	3 + 0	4 + 4	2 + 2	4 + 0

Practice all tricks.

5 + 1	4 + 4	3 – 1	0 + 1	2 + 1	5 + 0	1 + 9
10 – 1	0 + 2	4 + 4	5 + 5	7 + 1	7 – 1	3 + 1
3 + 3	1 + 2	1 + 6	8 + 0	4 + 1	9 – 1	7 + 0
4 + 4	8 – 1	2 – 1	1 + 4	2 + 2	0 + 6	5 – 1
6 + 1	4 – 1	0 + 9	4 + 4	1 + 1	8 + 1	6 – 1

Two Plus Two Is Not Five, Easy Methods To Learn Addition and Subtraction

Name _____

TRICK Doubles Subtraction

You know   5   Learn   10
         + 5   − 5
         10   5

You have

Take away 5.

What is left?
     10
   − 5
      5

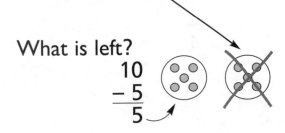

You know   2   Learn   4
         + 2   − 2
          4   2

You have

Take away 2.

What is left?
     4
   − 2
     2

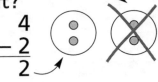

Learn **Doubles Subtraction**. What is the missing number?

5 + 5	2 + 2	2 + ___ 4	5 + ___ 10	2 + ___ 4	4 − 2	5 + ___ 10
10 − 5	4 − 2	1 + 1	5 + 5	5 + ___ 10	10 − 5	4 − 2
5 + 5	3 + 3	10 − ___ 5	2 + 2	2 + ___ 4	4 − 2	5 + 5
4 − 2	10 − 5	3 + 3	10 − 5	4 − 2	4 + 4	4 − 2

Name _____

Practice **Doubles** and **Number +1**.

4 + 4	2 + 1	4 + 1	10 − 5	4 − 2	6 + 1	4 − 2
3 + 3	4 − 2	5 + 5	8 + 1	1 + 5	10 − 5	1 + 9
7 + 1	10 − 5	3 + 1	4 − 2	1 + 2	3 + 3	4 + 4
9 + 1	1 + 8	5 + 5	10 − 5	4 + 4	10 − 5	1 + 7
3 + 3	1 + 1	1 + 6	4 − 2	5 + 1	2 + 2	1 + 3

Practice **Number +1**, **Backwards 1**, and **Zero**.

1 + 9	4 + 0	6 + 1	0 + 3	4 + 1	10 − 1	9 + 0
7 − 1	3 − 1	0 + 5	1 + 8	8 − 1	7 + 0	5 + 1
3 + 1	0 + 8	1 + 0	9 − 1	1 + 2	6 − 1	0 + 2

Two Plus Two Is Not Five, Easy Methods To Learn Addition and Subtraction   15

Name _____

Practice all tricks.

1 + 8	10 − 5	5 − 1	6 + 0	4 + 4	3 + 3	4 − 2
4 + 4	9 + 0	4 − 2	5 + 5	7 − 1	2 − 1	1 + 2
10 − 1	2 + 2	10 − 5	0 + 2	1 + 4	8 − 1	9 − 1
4 − 2	6 − 1	0 + 1	1 + 1	5 + 1	10 − 5	6 + 1

Try this way.

3−1= _____   4−2= _____   7+1= _____   10−5= _____

8+1= _____   2+1= _____   3+3= _____   7+0= _____

4−1= _____   5+5= _____   8+0= _____   4+4= _____

1+6= _____   1+3= _____   1+5= _____   10−1= _____

0+3= _____   10−5= _____   4−2= _____   9+1= _____

Name _____

TRICK   Right Next To Each Other

Mark) numbers next to each other.

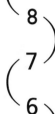

10)

9)
8)

6)
5)

Cross out if not next to each other.

~~10~~
~~4~~

~~6~~
~~3~~

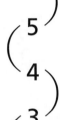

10)	~~8~~	7	4	10	10	5
9)	~~1~~	6	3	9	7	4

6	8	9	8	9	3	2
5	7	8	4	1	2	1

6	5	10	8	8	9	7
2	4	9	6	7	8	6

Right Next To Each Other = 1

$$\begin{array}{r} 10 \\ -\ 9 \\ \hline \end{array}$$

$$\begin{array}{r} 9 \\ -\ 8 \\ \hline \end{array}$$

$$\begin{array}{r} 4 \\ -\ 3 \\ \hline \end{array}$$

$$\begin{array}{r} 3 \\ -\ 2 \\ \hline \end{array}$$

$$\begin{array}{r} 7 \\ -\ 6 \\ \hline \end{array}$$

$$\begin{array}{r} 5 \\ -\ 4 \\ \hline \end{array}$$

$$\begin{array}{r} 8 \\ -\ 7 \\ \hline \end{array}$$

$$\begin{array}{r} 2 \\ -\ 1 \\ \hline \end{array}$$

$$\begin{array}{r} 6 \\ -\ 5 \\ \hline \end{array}$$

Two Plus Two Is Not Five, Easy Methods To Learn Addition and Subtraction   **17**

Name _____

If **Right Next to Each Other**, mark ⟩ and put the answer = 1.

If not, cross out.

4 ⟩	6̸	10	7	3	8	4
− 3	− 2̸	− 9	− 6	− 2	− 7	− 1
1						

5	6	10	4	9	5	7
− 4	− 5	− 2	− 3	− 8	− 3	− 6

8	9	5	8	10	2	6
− 7	− 8	− 4	− 4	− 9	− 1	− 5

Practice **Right Next to Each Other**, **Backwards 1**, and **Number +1**.

8	10	4	6	5	7	1
− 7	− 9	− 1	+ 1	− 4	− 1	+ 3

10	6	1	2	8	6	5
− 1	− 5	+ 7	+ 1	+ 1	− 1	− 4

3	4	5	8	7	1	10
− 1	− 3	+ 1	− 1	− 6	+ 4	− 9

9	9	4	8	1	1	4
− 1	− 8	+ 1	− 7	+ 8	+ 9	− 3

Two Plus Two Is Not Five, Easy Methods To Learn Addition and Subtraction

Name _____

Practice **Right Next to Each Other**, **Doubles**, and **Zero**.

3 −2	10 −9	0 +7	7 −6	3 +3	5 +5	4 +0
1 +1	4 +4	9 −8	6 −5	3 +0	10 −5	4 −2
4 −3	0 +9	3 +3	2 −1	8 −7	0 +2	4 −3
2 +2	10 −5	5 −4	4 +4	10 −9	4 −2	8 +0

Try all tricks this way.

7−6= _____   1+3= _____   6+0= _____   7−1= _____

9−8= _____   5+5= _____   6−5= _____   1+4= _____

0+1= _____   4−3= _____   3+3= _____   5−4= _____

5+1= _____   1+6= _____   8−7= _____   4−2= _____

10−5= _____   0+3= _____   3−2= _____   9−1= _____

Two Plus Two Is Not Five, Easy Methods To Learn Addition and Subtraction

Name _____

TRICK Doubles Subtraction

You know 3   Learn 6   You know 4   Learn 8

$$
\begin{array}{r} 3 \\ +\,3 \\ \hline 6 \end{array}
\qquad
\begin{array}{r} 6 \\ -\,3 \\ \hline 3 \end{array}
\qquad
\begin{array}{r} 4 \\ +\,4 \\ \hline 8 \end{array}
\qquad
\begin{array}{r} 8 \\ -\,4 \\ \hline 4 \end{array}
$$

What is the missing number?

$\begin{array}{r}3\\+\,3\\\hline\end{array}$	$\begin{array}{r}3\\+\,\underline{}\\\hline 6\end{array}$	$\begin{array}{r}6\\-\,3\\\hline\end{array}$	$\begin{array}{r}3\\+\,\underline{}\\\hline 6\end{array}$	$\begin{array}{r}4\\+\,4\\\hline\end{array}$	$\begin{array}{r}4\\+\,\underline{}\\\hline 8\end{array}$	$\begin{array}{r}8\\-\,4\\\hline\end{array}$
$\begin{array}{r}3\\+\,\underline{}\\\hline 6\end{array}$	$\begin{array}{r}4\\+\,4\\\hline\end{array}$	$\begin{array}{r}4\\+\,\underline{}\\\hline 8\end{array}$	$\begin{array}{r}8\\-\,4\\\hline\end{array}$	$\begin{array}{r}3\\+\,\underline{}\\\hline 6\end{array}$	$\begin{array}{r}6\\-\,3\\\hline\end{array}$	$\begin{array}{r}4\\+\,\underline{}\\\hline 8\end{array}$
$\begin{array}{r}8\\-\,4\\\hline\end{array}$	$\begin{array}{r}6\\-\,3\\\hline\end{array}$	$\begin{array}{r}8\\-\,4\\\hline\end{array}$	$\begin{array}{r}10\\-\,5\\\hline\end{array}$	$\begin{array}{r}6\\-\,3\\\hline\end{array}$	$\begin{array}{r}4\\-\,2\\\hline\end{array}$	$\begin{array}{r}8\\-\,4\\\hline\end{array}$

Practice **Doubles** and **Right Next to Each Other**.

$\begin{array}{r}6\\-\,3\\\hline\end{array}$	$\begin{array}{r}7\\-\,6\\\hline\end{array}$	$\begin{array}{r}3\\-\,2\\\hline\end{array}$	$\begin{array}{r}1\\+\,1\\\hline\end{array}$	$\begin{array}{r}8\\-\,4\\\hline\end{array}$	$\begin{array}{r}10\\-\,5\\\hline\end{array}$	$\begin{array}{r}8\\-\,7\\\hline\end{array}$
$\begin{array}{r}9\\-\,8\\\hline\end{array}$	$\begin{array}{r}8\\-\,4\\\hline\end{array}$	$\begin{array}{r}4\\-\,2\\\hline\end{array}$	$\begin{array}{r}6\\-\,5\\\hline\end{array}$	$\begin{array}{r}6\\-\,3\\\hline\end{array}$	$\begin{array}{r}2\\-\,1\\\hline\end{array}$	$\begin{array}{r}8\\-\,4\\\hline\end{array}$
$\begin{array}{r}8\\-\,4\\\hline\end{array}$	$\begin{array}{r}10\\-\,9\\\hline\end{array}$	$\begin{array}{r}6\\-\,3\\\hline\end{array}$	$\begin{array}{r}5\\+\,5\\\hline\end{array}$	$\begin{array}{r}8\\-\,4\\\hline\end{array}$	$\begin{array}{r}6\\-\,3\\\hline\end{array}$	$\begin{array}{r}2\\+\,2\\\hline\end{array}$

Two Plus Two Is Not Five, Easy Methods To Learn Addition and Subtraction

Name _____

Cumulative Practice.

8	5	1	7	3	10	8
− 4	+ 0	+ 4	+ 1	+ 3	− 5	− 1

1	3	10	8	6	9	5
+ 5	− 1	− 9	− 7	− 3	− 1	+ 5

6	3	7	1	10	4	4
− 3	− 2	− 1	+ 2	− 1	+ 4	− 3

4	1	9	6	3	0	8
− 2	+ 8	− 8	− 3	+ 1	+ 6	− 4

Practice this way.

$4-2=$ _____ $3+0=$ _____ $4-1=$ _____ $1+6=$ _____

$0+1=$ _____ $8-4=$ _____ $9+1=$ _____ $5-1=$ _____

$4+4=$ _____ $2-1=$ _____ $7-6=$ _____ $8+1=$ _____

$5+5=$ _____ $3+3=$ _____ $8-4=$ _____ $6-3=$ _____

$5-4=$ _____ $6-1=$ _____ $4+1=$ _____ $10-5=$ _____

Two Plus Two Is Not Five, Easy Methods To Learn Addition and Subtraction   **21**

Name _____

TRICK <u>Count by 2s</u> or <u>2 Ladder</u>

2   **4**   **6**   **8**   **10**

Practice **Count by 2s**.

2, 4, 6, 8, _____   2, 4, _____, 8, 10

2, _____, 6, _____, 10   2, 4, _____, 8, _____

_____, 4, 6, _____, _____   2, _____, _____, _____, 10

Count up by 2-steps.

```
10 ⤸ +2
 8 ⤸ +2
 6 ⤸ +2
 4 ⤸ +2
 2
```

Try <u>2 Ladder</u> addition.

2	4	6	8	6	4	8
+ 2	+ 2	+ 2	+ 2	+ 2	+ 2	+ 2

↑
(This is also <u>Doubles</u>.)

LOOK. These are the same.

```
 4            2
+ 2          + 4
 6            6
```

6	2	4	2	8	2	2
+ 2	+ 6	+ 2	+ 4	+ 2	+ 8	+ 6

Name _____

Practice **2 Ladder** and **Doubles**.

2 + 8	4 + 4	4 + 2	1 + 1	4 − 2	6 + 2	2 + 4
3 + 3	6 − 3	5 + 5	8 + 2	4 + 4	2 + 4	8 + 2
2 + 6	4 + 2	2 + 8	4 − 2	6 + 2	6 − 3	2 + 2
2 + 4	8 + 2	2 + 6	6 + 2	8 − 4	10 − 5	2 + 6

Practice **2 Ladder**, **Backwards 1**, and **Number +1**.

6 + 2	8 + 2	5 − 1	1 + 4	8 − 1	6 − 1	4 + 2
2 + 8	1 + 7	6 + 1	1 + 2	2 + 6	9 − 1	1 + 5
8 + 1	2 + 4	10 − 1	3 − 1	4 + 2	8 + 2	2 + 6
1 + 3	2 − 1	6 + 2	4 − 1	2 + 8	9 + 1	2 + 4

Two Plus Two Is Not Five, Easy Methods To Learn Addition and Subtraction 23

Name _____

Practice <u>2 Ladder</u> and <u>**Right Next to Each Other**</u>.

8 + 2	6 − 5	2 + 4	3 − 2	7 − 6	2 + 6	2 + 8
5 − 4	2 + 4	10 − 9	2 − 1	2 + 8	4 + 2	6 + 2
6 + 2	9 − 8	8 + 2	4 + 2	8 − 7	2 + 6	4 − 3

Cumulative Practice.

2 + 8	5 − 4	4 + 4	0 + 7	2 + 4	6 + 2	4 + 1
1 + 9	8 + 2	7 − 1	3 + 1	8 − 4	4 − 2	0 + 3
1 + 6	4 + 2	6 − 5	2 + 8	2 + 2	10 − 9	6 − 1
2 + 6	5 + 0	6 − 3	2 + 4	8 + 2	1 + 5	9 − 8
10 − 5	6 + 2	4 − 3	8 − 1	4 + 2	10 − 1	2 + 6

Tier 2

Instructions and Information

Start with any trick. The tricks may be introduced in any order except:

- The two **Double +1** sets of facts should be taught in the given sequence, but the second set does not immediately have to follow the first set.

- The two **Zero** sets of facts should be taught in the given sequence, but the second set does not immediately have to follow the first set.

- The two **Doubles** sets of facts should be taught in the given sequence, but the second set does not immediately have to follow the first set.

It is not necessary to assign all 18 of the **Zero** facts.

Page	Trick	Math fact cards to be assigned:
25-26	**Double +1**	2+3, 3+2
27-30	**Double +1**	3+4, 4+3
31-32	**Zero** (Number – Number)	9-9, 8-8, 7-7, 6-6, 5-5, 4-4, 3-3, 2-2, 1-1
33-34	**Doubles**	6+6, 12-6
35-38	**Doubles**	7+7, 14-7
39-40	**Zero** (Number – Zero)	9-0, 8-0, 7-0, 6-0, 5-0, 4-0, 3-0, 2-0, 1-0
41-44	**Number in the Middle**	3+5, 5+3, 4+6, 6+4
45-48	**Magic 9**	2+9, 3+9, 4+9, 5+9, 6+9, 7+9, 8+9 9+2, 9+3, 9+4, 9+5, 9+6, 9+7, 9+8, 9+9
49-56	**Review Pages**	

Tier 2 Answers

Page 25
5,5,4,5,5
4,5,10,5,5,2,4
8,4,5,10,4,6,5
5,3,2,5,9,5,6
4,5,9,7
5,5,5,2
8,5,5,6

Page 26
5,7,5,5,5,3,5
9,5,10,5,4,5,7
5,6,5,3,8,5,5
8,4,10,5,9,6,5
5,10,8,5,6,6,5
8,5,6,5,10,5,8
5,8,5,10,5,8,5
10,5,8,5,6,5,10

Page 27
7,6,7,6,7
6,7,6,7,7,4,5
7,4,5,7,7,5,5
5,7,6,5,10,7,5
10,3,7,9,5,3,7

Page 28
5,1,1,7,1,5,1
1,5,7,1,5,1,7
7,1,5,1,7,1,7
7,5,7,2
6,3,7,7
7,5,2,5
1,4,7,6
5,8,4,8
9,7,9,5
7,5,5,3
7,5,7,10

Page 29
5,10,6,7,8,6,5
7,8,7,6,5,10,7
8,5,7,10,8,7,10
5,8,10,8,6,7,8
6,9,8,1,5,10,7
7,5,4,4,7,5,5
1,3,3,7,6,4,5
5,8,7,10,6,7,7

Page 30
7,10,10,1,8,5,10
4,6,1,7,5,3,9
5,3,5,3,1,1,7
1,8,7,1,6,9,8
1,2,5,1,3,7,10
2,7,5,6,8,5,5
4,9,1,6,7,6,4

Page 31
0,0,0,2,0,8,0
0,10,0,4,0,0,6
0,1,5,0,2,4,0
3,0,0,9,0,8,0

Page 32
0,9,7,8
10,3,6,0
4,8,7,0
0,10,2,6
8,4,0,9
5,10,8,6
10,3,8,9,0,1,6
10,8,1,2,3,6,5
6,0,0,5,1,0,1
5,2,10,1,5,0,8

Page 33
12,6,12,10,4,8,12
2,10,6,12,8,12,4
12,8,4,10,12,6,2
12,6,6,12,6,6
12,6,8,6,5,6,3
6,4,12,2,4,6,10

Page 34
12,4,6,5
4,10,2,3
6,12,4,2
8,2,6,6
12,8,3,5
10,6,5,12
6,10,6,12,2,8,12
6,3,5,10,6,4,6
8,6,10,2,4,3,8
6,10,10,12,4,5,8

Page 35
14,8,14,12,6,14
10,4,14,6,2,14,12
14,7,7,14,7,7
14,7,6,14,7,12,8
7,6,2,3,10,7,14
4,14,4,6,7,6,5
10,3,7,8,14,4,7

Page 36
14,1,10,1,5,6,7
12,6,1,14,4,2,1
7,1,12,1,12,7,1
1,3,7,1,14,2,8
7,12,3,7,7,4,14
6,9,6,4,7,4,1
2,10,14,5,8,6,3
12,7,8,14,5,2,7

Page 37
12,7,5,8,6,14,5
7,10,14,4,6,4,7
6,10,9,14,6,12,8
3,7,4,6,7,3,14
4,6,7,10,10,8,12
4,6,8,6,8,14,6
10,2,12,5,8,6,3
6,10,14,2,7,6,8

Page 38
7,2,8,4,3,8,14
1,12,4,10,1,6,5
12,4,9,4,6,7,6
1,7,6,1,5,14,10
6,8,2,14,1,6,12
3,10,7,10,6,1,5
14,9,8,2,6,7,7
1,12,1,6,1,3,14

Page 39
9,8,2,9,6,9,0
5,7,1,4,4,3,3
8,2,0,2,6,8,0
5,0,1,1,7,4,4

Page 40
4,8,0,4,10,0,0
1,9,6,3,0,10,7
0,6,5,0,8,1,8
7,6,2,10,0,3,8
7,3,1,0,8,5,1
1,7,4,1,5,1,0
1,3,0,9,0,6,0

Page 41
2,5,3,4
4,2,5,3
2,5,4,5,4,5
4,8,8
5,10,10

Page 42
4,4,4
6,6,6
10,5,4,8,6,10,8
7,10,8,10,3,8,10
8,6,10,6,10,4,2
9,6,9,10,8,5,8

Page 43
10,1,6,8,6,6,9
7,8,3,10,4,5,4
8,2,10,8,8,6,10
9,5,8,10,7,2,6
8,1,6,1,1,8,10
8,6,1,10,8,1,1
1,10,10,10,1,6,8,1
1,8,1,10,1,6,10

Page 44
8,7,6,10,6,8,10
7,10,5,10,1,8,10
9,8,6,2,5,6,10
3,8,6,6,10,8,1
10,9,2,1
10,2,1,10
5,1,6,8
8,10,1,3
4,8,10,8
6,10,4,8
10,7,1,1

Page 45
7,4,2,6,8,5,1,3
16,17,13,15,11,14,12
17,17,12,12
13,13,18,15,11,16,14
12,15,16,17,14,13,11

Page 46
16,5,12,15,9,3,15
10,4,14,11,17,4,10
12,13,18,7,8,17,6
2,7,16,9,3,14,13
18,8,11,16,6,17,5
13,18,17,12
16,14,11,15
15,16,17,13
17,12,13,11
16,14,18,16

Page 47
15,7,14,1,6,13,2
16,12,4,7,17,5,9
15,3,8,12,14,16,13
11,2,18,15,11,8,17
14,16,15,1,1,11,1
17,1,1,1,18,1,1
12,1,12,13,16,15,18
11,1,17,1,14,1,13

Page 48
18,3,6,12,4,1,10
2,5,6,1,16,9,8
15,14,1,6,7,5,13
11,17,2,2,8,16,3
4,14,10,6
7,12,17,8
1,10,11,15
8,13,6,9
4,1,1,12

Page 49
7,5,8,7,10,8,5
6,7,10,10,7,6,8
5,10,7,8,5,10,7
7,7,14,13,5,17,11
5,16,7,12,15,5,7
18,7,5,16,7,14,5
7,13,17,5,12,5,7

Page 50
4,3,12,4,8,4,1
5,5,10,0,7,7,6
12,14,9,3,6,14,3
7,6,4,14,6,2,0
0,15,11,7,18,4,17
12,9,14,13,16,12,1
16,14,8,0,5,11,13
3,18,12,17,0,15,9

Page 51
6,16,4,13,14,4,5
7,15,14,10,7,12,14
3,12,17,8,14,11,7
14,7,6,5,2,6,12
8,10,14,8,6,12,8
8,5,10,6,6,3,10
12,7,4,14,10,7,6
4,8,3,10,8,4,6

Page 52
10,6,4,8,6,8,8
8,10,10,10,8,6,10
10,8,10,6,8,10,8
8,10,6,10,8,8,10
8,10,9,7,5,10,7
5,0,4,8,10,5,7
10,7,0,8,5,8,5
7,3,10,5,10,5,8

Page 53
12,2,6,16,8,18,7
17,5,15,3,13,4,14
1,11,17,16,14,13,11
12,14,2,15,3,18,15
17,10,8,16,13,6,14
15,10,12,6,8,11,12
8,18,10,13,6,18,10
14,11,8,16,15,17,6

Page 54
12,12,7,5,18,13,4
14,5,14,8,6,3,5
15,17,10,5,2,12,16
5,11,5,7,4,7,15
16,8,10,18,10,16,8
13,10,15,11,17,8,14
8,11,17,16,14,13,11
12,14,10,17,10,18,15

Page 55
10,5,12,1,6,5,6
10,3,14,12,8,8,7
7,8,8,7,6,0,5
3,6,4,5,13,7,10
7,5,10,5
9,10,10,1
5,17,3,2
2,7,6,8
9,14,8,6
1,8,8,15
7,16,0,5

Page 56
5,0,7,9,10,1,10
6,6,6,15,6,14,10
1,10,5,4,4,6,17
7,12,3,8,8,1,3
4,8,2,7
10,10,13,8
14,12,5,0
9,16,12,6
2,7,8,8
1,7,14,7
1,11,8,18

Name _____

TRICK Double +1   Looks like <u>Right Next to Each Other</u>.

Double the lesser number and add 1.

$$\begin{array}{r} ②\\ +\ 3\\ \hline 5 \end{array}$$
$$\begin{array}{r} 2\ \square\square\\ +\ 2\ \square\square\\ \hline 4 \end{array} + 1 \text{ more } \blacksquare = \begin{array}{r} 2\ \square\square\\ +\ 3\ \square\square\blacksquare\\ \hline 5 \end{array}$$
+ 1

LOOK. These are the same.

| $\begin{array}{r}②\\+\ 3\\\hline 5\end{array}$ $\begin{array}{r}3\\+\ ②\\\hline 5\end{array}$ | $\begin{array}{r}2\\+\ 3\\\hline\end{array}$ | $\begin{array}{r}3\\+\ 2\\\hline\end{array}$ | $\begin{array}{r}2\\+\ 2\\\hline\end{array}$ | $\begin{array}{r}3\\+\ 2\\\hline\end{array}$ | $\begin{array}{r}2\\+\ 3\\\hline\end{array}$ |

Practice these. Mark $)$ **Double +1**.

$$\begin{array}{r}2\\+\ 2\\\hline\end{array} \quad \begin{array}{r}3)\\+\ 2\\\hline\end{array} \quad \begin{array}{r}5\\+\ 5\\\hline\end{array} \quad \begin{array}{r}2)\\+\ 3\\\hline\end{array} \quad \begin{array}{r}3\\+\ 2\\\hline\end{array} \quad \begin{array}{r}1\\+\ 1\\\hline\end{array} \quad \begin{array}{r}2\\+\ 2\\\hline\end{array}$$

$$\begin{array}{r}4\\+\ 4\\\hline\end{array} \quad \begin{array}{r}2\\+\ 2\\\hline\end{array} \quad \begin{array}{r}2\\+\ 3\\\hline\end{array} \quad \begin{array}{r}9\\+\ 1\\\hline\end{array} \quad \begin{array}{r}2\\+\ 2\\\hline\end{array} \quad \begin{array}{r}3\\+\ 3\\\hline\end{array} \quad \begin{array}{r}3\\+\ 2\\\hline\end{array}$$

$$\begin{array}{r}2\\+\ 3\\\hline\end{array} \quad \begin{array}{r}4\\-\ 1\\\hline\end{array} \quad \begin{array}{r}2\\+\ 0\\\hline\end{array} \quad \begin{array}{r}2\\+\ 3\\\hline\end{array} \quad \begin{array}{r}1\\+\ 8\\\hline\end{array} \quad \begin{array}{r}3\\+\ 2\\\hline\end{array} \quad \begin{array}{r}5\\+\ 1\\\hline\end{array}$$

Try this way.

2+2 = _____   2+3 = _____   10−1 = _____   8−1 = _____

3+2 = _____   6−1 = _____   3+2 = _____   3−1 = _____

4+4 = _____   0+5 = _____   2+3 = _____   3+3 = _____

Two Plus Two Is Not Five, Easy Methods To Learn Addition and Subtraction   **25**

Name _____

Practice **Double +1** and **Number +1**.

2 + 3	6 + 1	3 + 2	4 + 1	3 + 2	1 + 2	2 + 3
8 + 1	3 + 2	1 + 9	3 + 2	3 + 1	2 + 3	1 + 6
3 + 2	1 + 5	2 + 3	2 + 1	7 + 1	3 + 2	1 + 4
1 + 7	1 + 3	9 + 1	2 + 3	1 + 8	5 + 1	2 + 3

Practice **Double +1** and **2 Ladder**.

3 + 2	2 + 8	6 + 2	2 + 3	4 + 2	2 + 4	2 + 3
2 + 6	3 + 2	4 + 2	3 + 2	8 + 2	2 + 3	6 + 2
3 + 2	2 + 6	2 + 3	8 + 2	3 + 2	2 + 6	2 + 3
2 + 8	2 + 3	6 + 2	3 + 2	2 + 4	3 + 2	8 + 2

Two Plus Two Is Not Five, Easy Methods To Learn Addition and Subtraction

Name _____

More **Double +1**.   Looks like <u>Right Next to Each Other</u>.

Double the lesser number and add 1.

③
$+ 4$
$\overline{}\ 7$

$\begin{array}{r}3 \\ + 3 \\ \hline 6 \end{array}$ □□□ □□□ $+ 1$ more ▨ $=$ $\begin{array}{r}3 \\ + 4 \\ \hline 7 \end{array}$ □□□ □□▨

+ 1

LOOK. These are the same.

③	**4**	4	3	4	3	3
$+ 4$	$+③$	$+ 3$	$+ 3$	$+ 3$	$+ 3$	$+ 4$
$\overline{7}$	$\overline{7}$					

Practice these. Mark $)$ **Double +1**.

3	3 $)$	3	4	3	2	2
$+ 3$	$+ 4$	$+ 3$	$+ 3$	$+ 4$	$+ 2$	$+ 3$

4	2	3	0	4	2	1
$+ 3$	$+ 2$	$+ 2$	$+ 7$	$+ 3$	$+ 3$	$+ 4$

3	3	3	2	9	4	3
$+ 2$	$+ 4$	$+ 3$	$+ 3$	$+ 1$	$+ 3$	$+ 2$

5	6	3	9	3	4	3
$+ 5$	$- 3$	$+ 4$	$- 0$	$+ 2$	$- 1$	$+ 4$

Two Plus Two Is Not Five, Easy Methods To Learn Addition and Subtraction   **27**

Name _____

Practice **Double +1** and **Right Next to Each Other**.

3 + 2	4 − 3	5 − 4	4 + 3	10 − 9	2 + 3	3 − 2
9 − 8	2 + 3	3 + 4	7 − 6	3 + 2	8 − 7	4 + 3
3 + 4	6 − 5	3 + 2	3 − 2	4 + 3	4 − 3	3 + 4

Practice **Double +1**, **Number +1**, and **Backwards 1**.

4+3= _____	3+2= _____	8−1= _____	1+1= _____
7−1= _____	2+1= _____	3+4= _____	4+3= _____
3+4= _____	2+3= _____	3−1= _____	6−1= _____
2−1= _____	5−1= _____	3+4= _____	5+1= _____
2+3= _____	9−1= _____	1+3= _____	7+1= _____
1+8= _____	4+3= _____	10−1= _____	3+2= _____
3+4= _____	1+4= _____	2+3= _____	4−1= _____
1+6= _____	3+2= _____	4+3= _____	9+1= _____

Name _____

Practice **Double +1** and **2 Ladder**.

2 + 3	8 + 2	2 + 4	4 + 3	2 + 6	4 + 2	3 + 2
4 + 3	6 + 2	3 + 4	4 + 2	2 + 3	2 + 8	3 + 4
6 + 2	3 + 2	3 + 4	8 + 2	2 + 6	4 + 3	2 + 8

Cumulative Practice.

2 + 3	6 + 2	5 + 5	1 + 7	4 + 2	3 + 4	0 + 8
3 + 3	9 + 0	2 + 6	10 - 9	3 + 2	8 + 2	3 + 4
4 + 3	3 + 2	5 - 1	8 - 4	4 + 3	10 - 5	1 + 4
4 - 3	6 - 3	0 + 3	3 + 4	5 + 1	2 + 2	2 + 3
3 + 2	9 - 1	4 + 3	1 + 9	7 - 1	6 + 1	3 + 4

Two Plus Two Is Not Five, Easy Methods To Learn Addition and Subtraction **29**

Name _____

Cumulative Practice.

4 + 3	2 + 8	9 + 1	4 − 3	1 + 7	2 + 3	8 + 2
3 + 1	6 + 0	5 − 4	8 − 1	3 + 2	6 − 3	10 − 1
10 − 5	1 + 2	3 + 2	4 − 1	9 − 8	7 − 6	3 + 4
2 − 1	4 + 4	3 + 4	3 − 2	2 + 4	1 + 8	6 + 2
10 − 9	4 − 2	2 + 3	8 − 7	2 + 1	3 + 4	5 + 5
1 + 1	1 + 6	6 − 1	4 + 2	2 + 6	5 + 0	3 + 2
5 − 1	0 + 9	6 − 5	3 + 3	4 + 3	1 + 5	8 − 4

Two Plus Two Is Not Five, Easy Methods To Learn Addition and Subtraction

Name _____

TRICK Learn more with <u>Zero</u>.

You have **3** candy bars.

Eat **3**. $\begin{array}{r} 3 \\ -\ 3 \\ \hline 0 \end{array}$ are left.

You have **5** candy bars.

Eat **5**. → $\begin{array}{r} 5 \\ -\ 5 \\ \hline 0 \end{array}$ are left.

You have **9** candy bars.

Eat **9**. → $\begin{array}{r} 9 \\ -\ 9 \\ \hline 0 \end{array}$ are left.

Practice.

$\begin{array}{r} 6 \\ -\ 6 \\ \hline \end{array}$	$\begin{array}{r} 4 \\ -\ 4 \\ \hline \end{array}$	$\begin{array}{r} 8 \\ -\ 8 \\ \hline \end{array}$	$\begin{array}{r} 1 \\ +\ 1 \\ \hline \end{array}$	$\begin{array}{r} 9 \\ -\ 9 \\ \hline \end{array}$	$\begin{array}{r} 4 \\ +\ 4 \\ \hline \end{array}$	$\begin{array}{r} 7 \\ -\ 7 \\ \hline \end{array}$
$\begin{array}{r} 3 \\ -\ 3 \\ \hline \end{array}$	$\begin{array}{r} 5 \\ +\ 5 \\ \hline \end{array}$	$\begin{array}{r} 1 \\ -\ 1 \\ \hline \end{array}$	$\begin{array}{r} 2 \\ +\ 2 \\ \hline \end{array}$	$\begin{array}{r} 2 \\ -\ 2 \\ \hline \end{array}$	$\begin{array}{r} 5 \\ -\ 5 \\ \hline \end{array}$	$\begin{array}{r} 3 \\ +\ 3 \\ \hline \end{array}$

Practice **Zero**.

$\begin{array}{r} 2 \\ -\ 2 \\ \hline \end{array}$	$\begin{array}{r} 0 \\ +\ 1 \\ \hline \end{array}$	$\begin{array}{r} 5 \\ +\ 0 \\ \hline \end{array}$	$\begin{array}{r} 4 \\ -\ 4 \\ \hline \end{array}$	$\begin{array}{r} 2 \\ +\ 0 \\ \hline \end{array}$	$\begin{array}{r} 0 \\ +\ 4 \\ \hline \end{array}$	$\begin{array}{r} 9 \\ -\ 9 \\ \hline \end{array}$
$\begin{array}{r} 3 \\ +\ 0 \\ \hline \end{array}$	$\begin{array}{r} 7 \\ -\ 7 \\ \hline \end{array}$	$\begin{array}{r} 6 \\ -\ 6 \\ \hline \end{array}$	$\begin{array}{r} 0 \\ +\ 9 \\ \hline \end{array}$	$\begin{array}{r} 5 \\ -\ 5 \\ \hline \end{array}$	$\begin{array}{r} 8 \\ +\ 0 \\ \hline \end{array}$	$\begin{array}{r} 8 \\ -\ 8 \\ \hline \end{array}$

Two Plus Two Is Not Five, Easy Methods To Learn Addition and Subtraction   **31**

Name _____

Practice **Zero**, **Backwards 1**, and **2 Ladder**.

5−5= _____	9+0= _____	8−1= _____	2+6= _____
8+2= _____	4−1= _____	2+4= _____	4−4= _____
5−1= _____	6+2= _____	0+7= _____	7−7= _____
1−1= _____	2+8= _____	3−1= _____	4+2= _____
8+0= _____	0+4= _____	2−2= _____	10−1= _____
6−1= _____	8+2= _____	9−1= _____	6+0= _____

Cumulative Practice.

8	0	4	8	3	10	2
+ 2	+ 3	+ 4	+ 1	− 3	− 9	+ 4

1	2	6	2	1	7	10
+ 9	+ 6	− 5	+ 0	+ 2	− 1	− 5

3	9	6	4	5	8	0
+ 3	− 9	− 6	+ 1	− 4	− 8	+ 1

6	4	2	4	5	1	6
− 1	− 2	+ 8	− 3	+ 0	− 1	+ 2

Name _____

TRICK Doubles

Learn

$$
\begin{array}{r}
6 \\
+\ 6 \\
\hline
12
\end{array}
$$

|1|2|3|4|5|6|
|7|8|9|10|11|12|

Practice.

| $\begin{array}{r}6\\+\ 6\end{array}$ | $\begin{array}{r}3\\+\ 3\end{array}$ | $\begin{array}{r}6\\+\ 6\end{array}$ | $\begin{array}{r}5\\+\ 5\end{array}$ | $\begin{array}{r}2\\+\ 2\end{array}$ | $\begin{array}{r}4\\+\ 4\end{array}$ | $\begin{array}{r}6\\+\ 6\end{array}$ |

| $\begin{array}{r}1\\+\ 1\end{array}$ | $\begin{array}{r}5\\+\ 5\end{array}$ | $\begin{array}{r}3\\+\ 3\end{array}$ | $\begin{array}{r}6\\+\ 6\end{array}$ | $\begin{array}{r}4\\+\ 4\end{array}$ | $\begin{array}{r}6\\+\ 6\end{array}$ | $\begin{array}{r}2\\+\ 2\end{array}$ |

| $\begin{array}{r}6\\+\ 6\end{array}$ | $\begin{array}{r}4\\+\ 4\end{array}$ | $\begin{array}{r}2\\+\ 2\end{array}$ | $\begin{array}{r}5\\+\ 5\end{array}$ | $\begin{array}{r}6\\+\ 6\end{array}$ | $\begin{array}{r}3\\+\ 3\end{array}$ | $\begin{array}{r}1\\+\ 1\end{array}$ |

Learn **Doubles Subtraction**. What is the missing number?

| $\begin{array}{r}\mathbf{12}\\-\ \mathbf{6}\\\hline\mathbf{6}\end{array}$ | $\begin{array}{r}6\\+\ 6\end{array}$ | $\begin{array}{r}6\\+\ \underline{}\\\hline12\end{array}$ | $\begin{array}{r}12\\-\ 6\end{array}$ | $\begin{array}{r}6\\+\ 6\end{array}$ | $\begin{array}{r}6\\+\ \underline{}\\\hline12\end{array}$ | $\begin{array}{r}12\\-\ 6\end{array}$ |

Practice **Doubles**.

| $\begin{array}{r}6\\+\ 6\end{array}$ | $\begin{array}{r}12\\-\ 6\end{array}$ | $\begin{array}{r}4\\+\ 4\end{array}$ | $\begin{array}{r}12\\-\ 6\end{array}$ | $\begin{array}{r}10\\-\ 5\end{array}$ | $\begin{array}{r}3\\+\ 3\end{array}$ | $\begin{array}{r}6\\-\ 3\end{array}$ |

| $\begin{array}{r}12\\-\ 6\end{array}$ | $\begin{array}{r}8\\-\ 4\end{array}$ | $\begin{array}{r}6\\+\ 6\end{array}$ | $\begin{array}{r}4\\-\ 2\end{array}$ | $\begin{array}{r}2\\+\ 2\end{array}$ | $\begin{array}{r}12\\-\ 6\end{array}$ | $\begin{array}{r}5\\+\ 5\end{array}$ |

Two Plus Two Is Not Five, Easy Methods To Learn Addition and Subtraction

Name _____

Practice **Doubles**.

6+6= _____	2+2= _____	12−6= _____	10−5= _____
8−4= _____	5+5= _____	4−2= _____	6−3= _____
12−6= _____	6+6= _____	8−4= _____	1+1= _____
4+4= _____	4−2= _____	3+3= _____	12−6= _____
6+6= _____	4+4= _____	6−3= _____	10−5= _____
5+5= _____	12−6= _____	10−5= _____	6+6= _____

Practice **Doubles** and **2 Ladder**.

12 − 6	2 + 8	4 + 2	6 + 6	4 − 2	6 + 2	6 + 6
3 + 3	6 − 3	10 − 5	8 + 2	12 − 6	8 − 4	2 + 4
2 + 6	12 − 6	2 + 8	4 − 2	2 + 2	6 − 3	4 + 4
2 + 4	8 + 2	5 + 5	6 + 6	8 − 4	10 − 5	2 + 6

Two Plus Two Is Not Five, Easy Methods To Learn Addition and Subtraction

Name _____

TRICK Learn more with <u>Doubles</u>.

7	7	4	7	6	3	7
+ 7	+ 7	+ 4	+ 7	+ 6	+ 3	+ 7
14						

5	2	7	3	1	7	6
+ 5	+ 2	+ 7	+ 3	+ 1	+ 7	+ 6

Learn **Doubles Subtraction**. What is the missing number?

14	7	7	14	7	7	14
− 7	+ 7	+ __	− 7	+ 7	+ __	− 7
7		14			14	

Practice **Doubles**.

7	14	3	7	14	6	4
+ 7	− 7	+ 3	+ 7	− 7	+ 6	+ 4

14	12	4	6	5	14	7
− 7	− 6	− 2	− 3	+ 5	− 7	+ 7

2	7	8	12	14	3	10
+ 2	+ 7	− 4	− 6	− 7	+ 3	− 5

5	6	14	4	7	8	14
+ 5	− 3	− 7	+ 4	+ 7	− 4	− 7

Two Plus Two Is Not Five, Easy Methods To Learn Addition and Subtraction   **35**

Name _____

Practice **Doubles** and **Right Next to Each Other**.

7 + 7	2 − 1	5 + 5	4 − 3	10 − 5	3 + 3	14 − 7
6 + 6	12 − 6	3 − 2	7 + 7	8 − 4	1 + 1	6 − 5
14 − 7	7 − 6	6 + 6	10 − 9	6 + 6	14 − 7	5 − 4
9 − 8	6 − 3	14 − 7	8 − 7	7 + 7	4 − 2	4 + 4

Practice **Doubles** and **Backwards 1**.

14 − 7	6 + 6	4 − 1	14 − 7	8 − 1	5 − 1	7 + 7
3 + 3	10 − 1	12 − 6	2 + 2	14 − 7	8 − 4	2 − 1
4 − 2	5 + 5	7 + 7	6 − 1	4 + 4	12 − 6	6 − 3
6 + 6	14 − 7	9 − 1	7 + 7	10 − 5	1 + 1	14 − 7

Two Plus Two Is Not Five, Easy Methods To Learn Addition and Subtraction

Name _____

Practice **Doubles** and **Number +1**.

6 + 6	14 − 7	10 − 5	1 + 7	3 + 3	7 + 7	4 + 1
14 − 7	1 + 9	7 + 7	3 + 1	12 − 6	8 − 4	14 − 7
12 − 6	5 + 5	8 + 1	7 + 7	5 + 1	6 + 6	4 + 4
1 + 2	14 − 7	8 − 4	12 − 6	6 + 1	6 − 3	7 + 7

Practice **Doubles** and **2 Ladder**.

8 − 4	4 + 2	14 − 7	8 + 2	5 + 5	2 + 6	6 + 6
2 + 2	3 + 3	6 + 2	4 + 2	4 + 4	7 + 7	12 − 6
2 + 8	4 − 2	6 + 6	10 − 5	6 + 2	2 + 4	6 − 3
12 − 6	8 + 2	7 + 7	1 + 1	14 − 7	3 + 3	2 + 6

Two Plus Two Is Not Five, Easy Methods To Learn Addition and Subtraction **37**

Name _____

Cumulative Practice.

14 − 7	3 − 1	2 + 6	0 + 4	1 + 2	9 − 1	7 + 7
10 − 9	6 + 6	2 + 2	1 + 9	8 − 7	12 − 6	1 + 4
6 + 6	3 + 1	10 − 1	8 − 4	5 + 1	8 − 1	3 + 3
7 − 6	14 − 7	2 + 4	5 − 4	5 + 0	7 + 7	5 + 5
12 − 6	4 + 4	1 + 1	7 + 7	3 − 2	4 + 2	6 + 6
3 + 0	8 + 2	14 − 7	2 + 8	12 − 6	2 − 1	10 − 5
7 + 7	8 + 1	6 + 2	4 − 2	7 − 1	14 − 7	0 + 7
4 − 3	6 + 6	6 − 5	12 − 6	9 − 8	6 − 3	7 + 7

Two Plus Two Is Not Five, Easy Methods To Learn Addition and Subtraction

Name _____

TRICK Learn more with <u>Zero</u>.

You have **3** candy bars.

Eat **0** candy bars. → $\begin{array}{r} 3 \\ -\ 0 \\ \hline 3 \end{array}$ are left.
You still have **3** candy bars.

You have **8** candy bars. $\begin{array}{r} 8 \\ -\ 0 \\ \hline 8 \end{array}$ are left.
Eat **0**. →

Practice **Zero** and **Backwards 1**.

$\begin{array}{r} 9 \\ -\ 0 \\ \hline \end{array}$ $\begin{array}{r} 8 \\ -\ 0 \\ \hline \end{array}$ $\begin{array}{r} 3 \\ -\ 1 \\ \hline \end{array}$ $\begin{array}{r} 10 \\ -\ 1 \\ \hline \end{array}$ $\begin{array}{r} 6 \\ -\ 0 \\ \hline \end{array}$ $\begin{array}{r} 9 \\ +\ 0 \\ \hline \end{array}$ $\begin{array}{r} 7 \\ -\ 7 \\ \hline \end{array}$

$\begin{array}{r} 6 \\ -\ 1 \\ \hline \end{array}$ $\begin{array}{r} 0 \\ +\ 7 \\ \hline \end{array}$ $\begin{array}{r} 1 \\ -\ 0 \\ \hline \end{array}$ $\begin{array}{r} 5 \\ -\ 1 \\ \hline \end{array}$ $\begin{array}{r} 4 \\ -\ 0 \\ \hline \end{array}$ $\begin{array}{r} 4 \\ -\ 1 \\ \hline \end{array}$ $\begin{array}{r} 3 \\ -\ 0 \\ \hline \end{array}$

$\begin{array}{r} 9 \\ -\ 1 \\ \hline \end{array}$ $\begin{array}{r} 2 \\ -\ 0 \\ \hline \end{array}$ $\begin{array}{r} 4 \\ -\ 4 \\ \hline \end{array}$ $\begin{array}{r} 2 \\ +\ 0 \\ \hline \end{array}$ $\begin{array}{r} 7 \\ -\ 1 \\ \hline \end{array}$ $\begin{array}{r} 0 \\ +\ 8 \\ \hline \end{array}$ $\begin{array}{r} 6 \\ -\ 6 \\ \hline \end{array}$

$\begin{array}{r} 5 \\ -\ 0 \\ \hline \end{array}$ $\begin{array}{r} 2 \\ -\ 2 \\ \hline \end{array}$ $\begin{array}{r} 2 \\ -\ 1 \\ \hline \end{array}$ $\begin{array}{r} 0 \\ +\ 1 \\ \hline \end{array}$ $\begin{array}{r} 8 \\ -\ 1 \\ \hline \end{array}$ $\begin{array}{r} 4 \\ +\ 0 \\ \hline \end{array}$ $\begin{array}{r} 5 \\ -\ 1 \\ \hline \end{array}$

Two Plus Two Is Not Five, Easy Methods To Learn Addition and Subtraction

Name _____

Practice **Zero** and **2 Ladder**.

4 + 0	2 + 6	9 − 9	4 − 0	8 + 2	6 − 6	5 − 5
0 + 1	9 + 0	4 + 2	0 + 3	3 − 3	2 + 8	7 − 0
8 − 8	2 + 4	5 + 0	4 − 4	6 + 2	1 − 0	8 + 0
0 + 7	6 − 0	0 + 2	8 + 2	7 − 7	3 − 0	2 + 6

Practice **Zero** and **Right Next to Each Other**.

7 − 0	3 − 0	8 − 7	5 − 5	8 − 0	0 + 5	5 − 4
6 − 5	7 + 0	4 − 0	4 − 3	5 − 0	10 − 9	3 − 3
7 − 6	3 + 0	9 − 9	0 + 9	8 − 8	6 + 0	1 − 1

Two Plus Two Is Not Five, Easy Methods To Learn Addition and Subtraction

Name _____

TRICK   Number in the Middle

What fits in the middle?

1 _____ 3   4 _____ 6   2 _____ 4   3 _____ 5

5 _____ 3   3 _____ 1   6 _____ 4   4 _____ 2

LOOK. This is the same.

1	6	5	6	3	4
◯	◯	◯	◯	◯	◯
3	4	3	4	5	6

Learn **Number in the Middle** with **Doubles**.

3 _____ 5

$$\begin{array}{r} 3 \\ \cdots \\ + 5 \\ \hline 8 \end{array}$$ → 4 fits in the middle. $\begin{array}{r} 3 \\ + 5 \end{array}$ $\begin{array}{r} 3+1 \\ 5-1 \end{array}$ Double 4. $\begin{array}{r} 4 \\ + 4 \end{array}$

4 _____ 6

$$\begin{array}{r} 4 \\ \cdots \\ + 6 \\ \hline 10 \end{array}$$ → 5 fits in the middle. $\begin{array}{r} 4 \\ + 6 \end{array}$ $\begin{array}{r} 4+1 \\ 6-1 \end{array}$ Double 5. $\begin{array}{r} 5 \\ + 5 \end{array}$

Name _____

More **Number in the Middle**

You already know these facts.

$\begin{array}{r} 1 \\ + 3 \\ \hline \end{array}$ → 2 fits in the middle.   Double 2 = _____. $\begin{array}{r} 2 \\ + 2 \\ \hline \end{array}$

↑ (This is also Number +1.)

$\begin{array}{r} 2 \\ + 4 \\ \hline \end{array}$ → 3 fits in the middle.   Double 3 = _____. $\begin{array}{r} 3 \\ + 3 \\ \hline \end{array}$

↑ (This is also 2 Ladder.)

Look. These are the same.

$\begin{array}{r} 4 \\ + 2 \\ \hline 6 \end{array}$ 3+3 $\begin{array}{r} 6 \\ + 4 \\ \hline 10 \end{array}$ 5+5 $\begin{array}{r} 3 \\ + 1 \\ \hline 4 \end{array}$ 2+2 $\begin{array}{r} 5 \\ + 3 \\ \hline 8 \end{array}$ 4+4

Try **Number in the Middle** and **Number +1**. Mark — **Number in the Middle**.

$\begin{array}{r} 4 \\ + 6 \\ \hline \end{array}$	$\begin{array}{r} 4 \\ + 1 \\ \hline \end{array}$	$\begin{array}{r} 1 \\ + 3 \\ \hline \end{array}$	$\begin{array}{r} 5 \\ + 3 \\ \hline \end{array}$	$\begin{array}{r} 4 \\ + 2 \\ \hline \end{array}$	$\begin{array}{r} 4 \\ + 6 \\ \hline \end{array}$	$\begin{array}{r} 3 \\ + 5 \\ \hline \end{array}$
$\begin{array}{r} 1 \\ + 6 \\ \hline \end{array}$	$\begin{array}{r} 6 \\ + 4 \\ \hline \end{array}$	$\begin{array}{r} 5 \\ + 3 \\ \hline \end{array}$	$\begin{array}{r} 1 \\ + 9 \\ \hline \end{array}$	$\begin{array}{r} 2 \\ + 1 \\ \hline \end{array}$	$\begin{array}{r} 7 \\ + 1 \\ \hline \end{array}$	$\begin{array}{r} 6 \\ + 4 \\ \hline \end{array}$
$\begin{array}{r} 3 \\ + 5 \\ \hline \end{array}$	$\begin{array}{r} 5 \\ + 1 \\ \hline \end{array}$	$\begin{array}{r} 4 \\ + 6 \\ \hline \end{array}$	$\begin{array}{r} 2 \\ + 4 \\ \hline \end{array}$	$\begin{array}{r} 6 \\ + 4 \\ \hline \end{array}$	$\begin{array}{r} 3 \\ + 1 \\ \hline \end{array}$	$\begin{array}{r} 1 \\ + 1 \\ \hline \end{array}$
$\begin{array}{r} 8 \\ + 1 \\ \hline \end{array}$	$\begin{array}{r} 4 \\ + 2 \\ \hline \end{array}$	$\begin{array}{r} 1 \\ + 8 \\ \hline \end{array}$	$\begin{array}{r} 4 \\ + 6 \\ \hline \end{array}$	$\begin{array}{r} 3 \\ + 5 \\ \hline \end{array}$	$\begin{array}{r} 1 \\ + 4 \\ \hline \end{array}$	$\begin{array}{r} 5 \\ + 3 \\ \hline \end{array}$

Name _____

Practice **Number in the Middle** and **Backwards 1**.

6 + 4	2 − 1	2 + 4	3 + 5	4 + 2	7 − 1	10 − 1
8 − 1	5 + 3	4 − 1	4 + 6	5 − 1	6 − 1	1 + 3
3 + 5	3 − 1	4 + 6	9 − 1	5 + 3	4 + 2	6 + 4
10 − 1	6 − 1	3 + 5	6 + 4	8 − 1	3 − 1	2 + 4

Practice **Number in the Middle** and **Right Next to Each Other**.

3 + 5	10 − 9	4 + 2	7 − 6	8 − 7	5 + 3	4 + 6
5 + 3	2 + 4	9 − 8	6 + 4	5 + 3	5 − 4	3 − 2
4 − 3	4 + 6	6 + 4	2 − 1	4 + 2	3 + 5	4 − 3
6 − 5	5 + 3	5 − 4	6 + 4	10 − 9	4 + 2	4 + 6

Two Plus Two Is Not Five, Easy Methods To Learn Addition and Subtraction **43**

Name _____

Cumulative Practice. Mark — **Number in the Middle**.

3 + 5	8 − 1	3 + 3	6 + 4	2 + 4	4 + 4	9 + 1

0 + 7	4 + 6	10 − 5	2 + 8	9 − 8	5 + 3	5 + 5

1 + 8	3 + 5	6 + 0	4 − 2	6 − 1	4 + 2	6 + 4

4 − 1	6 + 2	4 + 2	1 + 5	4 + 6	5 + 3	5 − 4

Try this way.

4+6= _____   10−1= _____   2+0= _____   3−2= _____

5+5= _____   4−2= _____   6−5= _____   6+4= _____

0+5= _____   4−3= _____   2+4= _____   3+5= _____

5+3= _____   4+6= _____   8−7= _____   6−3= _____

2+2= _____   3+5= _____   4+6= _____   2+6= _____

3+3= _____   8+2= _____   8−4= _____   5+3= _____

6+4= _____   6+1= _____   10−9= _____   7−6= _____

Name _____

TRICK Magic 9 with one less.

Write the number that is one less.

8	5	3	7	9	6	2	4
☐	☐	☐	☐	☐	☐	☐	☐

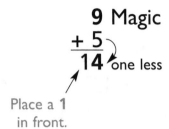

    9 Magic   **9** Magic   **9** Magic
  + **8** ⌐   + **5** ⌐   + **9** ⌐
  ‾‾‾‾‾‾‾   ‾‾‾‾‾‾‾   ‾‾‾‾‾‾‾
  17 ⌐one less   **14** ⌐one less   **18** ⌐one less

Place a **1**   Place a **1**   Place a **1**
in front.   in front.   in front.

Try **Magic 9**. Circle ⑨ .

⑨	9	9	9	9	9	9
+ 7	+ 8	+ 4	+ 6	+ 2	+ 5	+ 3

Look. These are the same.

9	5		Try.	9	8	9	3
+ 5	+ 9			+ 8	+ 9	+ 3	+ 9
14	14						

9	4	9	6	2	9	5
+ 4	+ 9	+ 9	+ 9	+ 9	+ 7	+ 9

3	9	7	8	9	4	9
+ 9	+ 6	+ 9	+ 9	+ 5	+ 9	+ 2

Two Plus Two Is Not Five, Easy Methods To Learn Addition and Subtraction **45**

Name _____

Practice **Magic 9** and **Number +1**.

9 + 7	4 + 1	9 + 3	9 + 6	1 + 8	2 + 1	6 + 9
9 + 1	1 + 3	9 + 5	2 + 9	9 + 8	3 + 1	1 + 9
3 + 9	4 + 9	9 + 9	6 + 1	1 + 7	8 + 9	5 + 1
1 + 1	1 + 6	7 + 9	8 + 1	1 + 2	5 + 9	9 + 4
9 + 9	7 + 1	9 + 2	9 + 7	1 + 5	8 + 9	1 + 4

Practice **Magic 9** this way.

4+9= _____	9+9= _____	8+9= _____	3+9= _____
9+7= _____	5+9= _____	9+2= _____	9+6= _____
6+9= _____	7+9= _____	9+8= _____	9+4= _____
9+8= _____	9+3= _____	4+9= _____	2+9= _____
7+9= _____	9+5= _____	9+9= _____	9+7= _____

Name _____

Practice **Magic 9** and **Backwards 1**.

9	8	5	2	7	9	3
+ 6	− 1	+ 9	− 1	− 1	+ 4	− 1

7	3	5	8	8	6	10
+ 9	+ 9	− 1	− 1	+ 9	− 1	− 1

6	4	9	9	9	9	4
+ 9	− 1	− 1	+ 3	+ 5	+ 7	+ 9

9	3	9	9	2	9	9
+ 2	− 1	+ 9	+ 6	+ 9	− 1	+ 8

Practice **Magic 9** and **Right Next to Each Other**.

9	9	6	2	7	9	3
+ 5	+ 7	+ 9	− 1	− 6	+ 2	− 2

8	9	5	8	9	6	10
+ 9	− 8	− 4	− 7	+ 9	− 5	− 9

3	4	9	9	7	9	9
+ 9	− 3	+ 3	+ 4	+ 9	+ 6	+ 9

2	3	9	6	5	9	4
+ 9	− 2	+ 8	− 5	+ 9	− 8	+ 9

Name _____

Cumulative Practice.

$$\begin{array}{r} 9 \\ +9 \\ \hline \end{array} \qquad \begin{array}{r} 1 \\ +2 \\ \hline \end{array} \qquad \begin{array}{r} 7 \\ -1 \\ \hline \end{array} \qquad \begin{array}{r} 3 \\ +9 \\ \hline \end{array} \qquad \begin{array}{r} 2 \\ +2 \\ \hline \end{array} \qquad \begin{array}{r} 9 \\ -8 \\ \hline \end{array} \qquad \begin{array}{r} 2 \\ +8 \\ \hline \end{array}$$

$$\begin{array}{r} 0 \\ +2 \\ \hline \end{array} \qquad \begin{array}{r} 10 \\ -5 \\ \hline \end{array} \qquad \begin{array}{r} 3 \\ +3 \\ \hline \end{array} \qquad \begin{array}{r} 5 \\ -4 \\ \hline \end{array} \qquad \begin{array}{r} 7 \\ +9 \\ \hline \end{array} \qquad \begin{array}{r} 8 \\ +1 \\ \hline \end{array} \qquad \begin{array}{r} 4 \\ +4 \\ \hline \end{array}$$

$$\begin{array}{r} 9 \\ +6 \\ \hline \end{array} \qquad \begin{array}{r} 5 \\ +9 \\ \hline \end{array} \qquad \begin{array}{r} 8 \\ -7 \\ \hline \end{array} \qquad \begin{array}{r} 2 \\ +4 \\ \hline \end{array} \qquad \begin{array}{r} 6 \\ +1 \\ \hline \end{array} \qquad \begin{array}{r} 5 \\ +0 \\ \hline \end{array} \qquad \begin{array}{r} 4 \\ +9 \\ \hline \end{array}$$

$$\begin{array}{r} 2 \\ +9 \\ \hline \end{array} \qquad \begin{array}{r} 8 \\ +9 \\ \hline \end{array} \qquad \begin{array}{r} 1 \\ +1 \\ \hline \end{array} \qquad \begin{array}{r} 4 \\ -2 \\ \hline \end{array} \qquad \begin{array}{r} 9 \\ -1 \\ \hline \end{array} \qquad \begin{array}{r} 9 \\ +7 \\ \hline \end{array} \qquad \begin{array}{r} 6 \\ -3 \\ \hline \end{array}$$

Try this way.

1+3= _____   9+5= _____   8+2= _____   6+0= _____

8−1= _____   9+3= _____   9+8= _____   7+1= _____

6−5= _____   5+5= _____   9+2= _____   6+9= _____

6+2= _____   9+4= _____   4+2= _____   10−1= _____

0+4= _____   2−1= _____   10−9= _____   3+9= _____

Two Plus Two Is Not Five, Easy Methods To Learn Addition and Subtraction

Name _____

Tiers 1 and 2 Review
Review **Double +1** and **Number in the Middle**.

4 + 3	2 + 3	5 + 3	3 + 4	6 + 4	3 + 5	3 + 2
2 + 4	4 + 3	4 + 6	6 + 4	3 + 4	4 + 2	5 + 3
3 + 2	6 + 4	3 + 4	3 + 5	2 + 3	4 + 6	4 + 3

Review **Double +1** and **Magic 9**.

3 + 4	4 + 3	5 + 9	9 + 4	2 + 3	8 + 9	9 + 2
3 + 2	9 + 7	4 + 3	3 + 9	9 + 6	3 + 2	3 + 4
9 + 9	3 + 4	2 + 3	7 + 9	4 + 3	9 + 5	2 + 3
4 + 3	4 + 9	9 + 8	2 + 3	9 + 3	3 + 2	3 + 4

Two Plus Two Is Not Five, Easy Methods To Learn Addition and Subtraction **49**

Name _____

Tiers 1 and 2 Review
Review **Zero** and **Doubles**.

4 + 0	6 − 3	6 + 6	2 + 2	4 + 4	8 − 4	0 + 1
10 − 5	0 + 5	5 + 5	6 − 6	14 − 7	7 − 0	12 − 6
6 + 6	7 + 7	9 − 0	3 + 0	12 − 6	7 + 7	6 − 3
14 − 7	3 + 3	8 − 4	7 + 7	6 + 0	4 − 2	2 − 2

Review **Zero** and **Magic 9**.

3 − 3	9 + 6	2 + 9	7 + 0	9 + 9	4 − 0	9 + 8
9 + 3	0 + 9	9 + 5	4 + 9	9 + 7	3 + 9	1 − 0
7 + 9	9 + 5	8 − 0	7 − 7	0 + 5	9 + 2	9 + 4
3 + 0	9 + 9	3 + 9	8 + 9	4 − 4	6 + 9	9 − 0

Two Plus Two Is Not Five, Easy Methods To Learn Addition and Subtraction

Name _____

Tiers 1 and 2 Review
Review **Doubles** and **Magic 9**.

12 − 6	7 + 9	8 − 4	9 + 4	5 + 9	2 + 2	10 − 5
14 − 7	9 + 6	7 + 7	5 + 5	14 − 7	3 + 9	7 + 7
6 − 3	6 + 6	9 + 8	4 + 4	7 + 7	2 + 9	14 − 7
5 + 9	14 − 7	3 + 3	10 − 5	4 − 2	12 − 6	9 + 3

Review **Doubles** and **Number in the Middle**.

4 + 4	4 + 6	7 + 7	5 + 3	4 + 2	6 + 6	3 + 5
5 + 3	10 − 5	6 + 4	3 + 3	12 − 6	6 − 3	4 + 6
6 + 6	14 − 7	8 − 4	7 + 7	6 + 4	14 − 7	2 + 4
8 − 4	3 + 5	6 − 3	4 + 6	5 + 3	2 + 2	12 − 6

Two Plus Two Is Not Five, Easy Methods To Learn Addition and Subtraction **51**

Name _____

Tiers 1 and 2 Review

Review **Number in the Middle** and **2 Ladder**.

4 + 6	2 + 4	1 + 3	5 + 3	4 + 2	6 + 2	3 + 5
5 + 3	2 + 8	6 + 4	8 + 2	6 + 2	2 + 4	4 + 6
6 + 4	3 + 5	8 + 2	4 + 2	2 + 6	2 + 8	5 + 3
2 + 6	6 + 4	2 + 4	4 + 6	3 + 5	6 + 2	8 + 2

Review **Number in the Middle**, **Zero**, and **Double +1**.

3 + 5	4 + 6	9 + 0	3 + 4	2 + 3	6 + 4	0 + 7
3 + 2	2 − 2	4 − 0	5 + 3	4 + 6	3 + 2	4 + 3
6 + 4	4 + 3	6 − 6	5 + 3	2 + 3	3 + 5	5 + 0
3 + 4	0 + 3	4 + 6	3 + 2	6 + 4	5 − 0	5 + 3

Name _____

Tiers 1 and 2 Review
Review **Magic 9** and **Backwards 1**.

9 + 3	3 − 1	7 − 1	7 + 9	9 − 1	9 + 9	8 − 1
9 + 8	6 − 1	6 + 9	4 − 1	9 + 4	5 − 1	9 + 5
2 − 1	9 + 2	8 + 9	9 + 7	9 + 5	9 + 4	2 + 9
3 + 9	5 + 9	3 − 1	6 + 9	4 − 1	9 + 9	9 + 6

Review **Magic 9** and **2 Ladder**.

8 + 9	2 + 8	2 + 6	7 + 9	9 + 4	4 + 2	9 + 5
9 + 6	8 + 2	9 + 3	4 + 2	6 + 2	9 + 2	3 + 9
2 + 6	9 + 9	8 + 2	4 + 9	2 + 4	9 + 9	2 + 8
5 + 9	2 + 9	6 + 2	9 + 7	6 + 9	9 + 8	2 + 4

Two Plus Two Is Not Five, Easy Methods To Learn Addition and Subtraction **53**

Name _____

Tiers 1 and 2 Review
Review **Magic 9**, **Double +1**, and **Doubles**.

9 + 3	6 + 6	3 + 4	10 − 5	9 + 9	4 + 9	2 + 2
7 + 7	3 + 2	9 + 5	4 + 4	12 − 6	6 − 3	2 + 3
6 + 9	9 + 8	5 + 5	3 + 2	4 − 2	6 + 6	9 + 7
2 + 3	2 + 9	3 + 2	14 − 7	8 − 4	4 + 3	9 + 6

Review **Magic 9** and **Number in the Middle**.

7 + 9	3 + 5	6 + 4	9 + 9	4 + 6	7 + 9	3 + 5
4 + 9	6 + 4	6 + 9	9 + 2	9 + 8	5 + 3	9 + 5
5 + 3	9 + 2	8 + 9	9 + 7	5 + 9	9 + 4	2 + 9
3 + 9	5 + 9	6 + 4	8 + 9	4 + 6	9 + 9	9 + 6

Name _____

Tiers 1 and 2 Review

Review all tricks.

8 + 2	3 + 2	6 + 6	10 − 9	1 + 5	5 + 0	12 − 6

4 + 6	0 + 3	7 + 7	9 + 3	2 + 6	4 + 4	4 + 3

14 − 7	6 + 2	5 + 3	8 − 1	2 + 4	9 − 9	2 + 3

3 − 0	3 + 3	8 − 4	4 + 1	9 + 4	3 + 4	6 + 4

14−7= _____   2+3= _____   5+5= _____   6−1= _____

8+1= _____   6+4= _____   2+8= _____   5−4= _____

10−5= _____   8+9= _____   6−3= _____   4−2= _____

0+2= _____   4+3= _____   4+2= _____   3+5= _____

10−1= _____   7+7= _____   1+7= _____   12−6= _____

9−8= _____   2+6= _____   5+3= _____   6+9= _____

3+4= _____   9+7= _____   7−7= _____   3+2= _____

Two Plus Two Is Not Five, Easy Methods To Learn Addition and Subtraction **55**

Name _____

Tiers 1 and 2 Review
Review all tricks.

3 + 2	5 – 5	6 + 1	10 – 1	1 + 9	4 – 3	2 + 8

12 – 6	7 – 1	6 – 0	9 + 6	2 + 4	7 + 7	6 + 4

7 – 6	8 + 2	10 – 5	5 – 1	2 + 2	5 + 1	9 + 8

4 + 3	6 + 6	2 + 1	0 + 8	5 + 3	8 – 7	6 – 3

1+3= _____   6+2= _____   1+1= _____   14–7= _____

9+1= _____   4+6= _____   4+9= _____   7+1= _____

7+7= _____   3+9= _____   2+3= _____   3–3= _____

1+8= _____   7+9= _____   6+6= _____   4+2= _____

2–0= _____   14–7= _____   2+6= _____   5+3= _____

10–9= _____   3+4= _____   9+5= _____   7+0= _____

3–2= _____   9+2= _____   3+5= _____   9+9= _____

Tier 3

Instructions and Information

Start with any trick. The tricks may be introduced in any order except:

- The two **Doubles** sets of facts should be taught in the given sequence, but the second set does not immediately have to follow the first set.

Page	Trick	Math fact cards to be assigned:
57-60	**Count by 3s**	3+6, 6+3, 9-3, 9-6
61-62	**Doubles**	8+8, 16-8
63-64	**Doubles Subtraction**	18-9
65-68	**Family Partners**	5-2, 5-3
69-72	**2 Ladder**	10-2, 8-2, 6-2
73-76	**Double +1**	4+5, 5+4
77-80	**Family Partners**	7-3, 7-4
81-84	**Curvy Numbers**	5+8, 8+5, 8-3, 8-5, 13-5, 13-8
85-96	**Review Pages**	

Tier 3 Answers

Page 57
9,6,9,6,6,9
9,3,3,9,3,6,9
6,3,9,7,9,10,3
2,9,3,8,5,3,9
3,6,7,9,4,6,8
9,4,9,3,8,6,9

Page 58
6,9,5,9,4,0,3
9,7,0,9,6,5,9
3,3,8,6,0,9,9
3,0,9,3,9,6,0
9,6,1,3,9,1,9
3,1,1,6,9,1,3
1,9,6,1,3,1,9
1,6,1,9,1,9,1

Page 59
9,9,6,8,6,3,8
10,3,8,6,10,9,6
9,8,10,6,9,3,10
6,9,8,3,8,9,6
9,11,3,14,6,12,13
6,12,9,15,13,3,9
17,6,18,9,16,11,9
9,15,3,14,17,6,16

Page 60
6,6,9,14,10,7,15
0,6,4,8,3,6,7
12,13,8,1,9,18,3
8,10,5,9,6,5,1
8,1,6,17,0,8,10
2,9,1,3,5,7,4
12,9,4,10,11,7,6

Page 61
16,8,16,10,4,16
2,14,16,6,12,16,14
16,8,8,16,8,8
8,14,8,7,16,5,3
16,8,16,6,8,2,16
7,12,14,8,10,16,8
8,4,4,16,3,8,6

Page 62
16,8,6,8,10,14,7
8,8,16,14,8,10,4
5,8,10,7,6,3,8
8,16,12,10,14,4,8
7,10,2,16,10,8,6
5,16,4,0
8,14,9,8
8,6,10,3
7,0,2,3
16,4,8,2

Page 63
18,9,9,4,9,16
18,9,9,18,9,12,18
9,9,5,9,8,9,14
18,7,9,10,9,6,16
8,9,6,4,7,9,8
9,16,18,8
4,14,12,8
3,7,8,9
5,9,6,16

Page 64
9,6,5,5,18,9,8
4,5,9,14,12,10,7
8,16,3,9,9,18,7
8,9,4,8,17,5,7
8,7,6,5,14,1,11
5,6,9,16,8,8,18
4,13,7,6,5,8,0
10,16,1,10,10,8,7

Page 65
3
5,2,3,5,2,5,3
6,3,5,2,5,3,2
2,3,2,5,3,5,2
4,3,5,3,5,2,3

Page 66
3,18,5,15,2,7,17
6,3,3,16,5,14,4
2,11,9,3,15,5,3
13,8,3,12,2,17,2
5,1,3,1,2,1,1
2,5,1,1,5,1,1
1,3,5,1,1,5,3
2,1,3,1,2,1,5

Page 67
5,2,10,3,6,10,8
3,8,2,5,8,3,10
10,5,8,2,10,6,8
6,3,10,5,6,8,2
2,5,8,3,9,5,7
9,5,0,10,2,4,3
5,5,3,4,8,0,2
3,7,5,3,0,5,4

Page 68
12,5,10,0,2,4,1
3,9,8,8,3,5,2
10,2,6,3,15,10,5
2,7,6,5,2,3,1
5,2,7,14,8,3,5
10,10,9,3,2,13,10
3,7,8,8,14,3,1

Page 69
8,6,2,8,4,6,2,4
8,6,8,4,8,6,4
6,2,4,8,6,4,2
8,8,10,6,4,8,8
4,6,10,4,6,6,8
4,8,8,6,2,4,6

Page 70
6,6,10,8
2,4,8,8
10,6,6,4
8,6,6,8,8,10,4
10,1,4,6,2,8,10
6,8,10,8,4,6,8
4,6,8,10,4,6,6

Page 71
8,15,6,13,10,8,4
6,11,18,6,16,8,14
8,17,10,2,8,13,6
4,10,15,4,12,8,8
6,8,6,10,0,1,8
4,7,6,4,10,4,6
8,2,8,8,8,4,5
0,6,10,6,2,8,6

Page 72
10,1,4,8,6,1,8
1,8,6,1,10,1,6
8,2,1,8,1,10,1
8,1,6,6,1,2,4
10,8,4,8,8,10,6
10,6,2,8,6,10,8
6,8,8,10,8,10,4
10,6,8,10,8,8,8

Page 73
9,9,8,9,9
8,9,4,5,9,9,7
6,7,9,9,2,9,5
4,9,1,9,5,7,12
7,3,9,6,5,5,9
1,9,5,9,7,9,0

Page 74
9,5,5,6,7,7,7
9,9,7,4,4,9,10
7,9,3,5,3,9,5
8,5,9,6,5,8,9
5,14,7,12
11,9,15,7
9,13,16,5
17,5,9,16
7,18,17,9
15,9,5,14

Page 75
7,1,5,1,9,1,9
7,1,9,5,1,7,5
1,1,7,1,7,9,1
5,9,9,1,5,1,5
9,8,3,7
0,5,7,10
0,9,8,0
5,7,0,10
9,10,8,9
6,7,8,9

Page 76
7,13,8,0,7,5,1
8,3,7,8,10,10,9
11,8,5,9,16,8,7
10,1,6,10,5,12,7
5,14,8,2,1,7,10
8,9,6,2,15,7,1
6,7,9,10,4,9,8,
3,9,1,12,8,14,0

Page 77
3,4 or 4,3
4,3
7,4,4,7,3,3,4
3,3,8,4,3,3,4
7,7,4,10,4,10,3
7,4,3,0,1,4,7

Page 78
7,4,0,3,4,7,6
3,0,7,9,5,4,7
7,7,3,3,4,7,0
1,4,7,4,7,5,3
7,3,10,4
8,8,4,7
4,10,8,3
10,4,10,7
3,7,4,8
6,10,8,3

Page 79
7,14,7,4
15,13,3,18
12,4,14,12
7,11,7,3
17,16,4,7
3,7,15,4
13,3,16,17
4,1,3,3,1,7,9
1,3,1,7,4,8,1
7,5,3,1,1,7,3
4,4,6,7,1,4,7

Page 80
7,8,18,1,7,4,6
3,10,14,8,3,12,0
11,7,14,4,11,8,5
1,3,6,10,6,4,8
7,1,12,13,4,16,1
9,10,4,4,8,10,7
7,5,7,7,3,3,15

Page 81
8,13,3,8,13,5,5
13,8,8,5,8,13,3
5,8,5,3,13,8,5

Page 82
8,8,0,13,8,5,9
8,5,3,3,5,8,3
5,13,5,3,13,8,8
5,0,8,13,0,3,13
13,1,8,1,5,1,13
1,5,8,13,3,13,5
1,8,13,1,5,3,1
13,8,5,8,1,5,3

Page 83
5,14,8,8,5,17,13
17,3,13,13,11,13,8
12,5,11,14,13,3,15
13,8,15,5,16,8,8
5,6,9,5
4,13,5,5
3,8,1,3
3,8,13,7
8,2,5,8
13,3,4,13
5,8,3,9

Page 84
13,10,8,13,10,5,5
8,6,5,10,8,8,3
8,13,6,5,13,10,8
0,8,7,10,13,2,10
13,5,12,3,14,1,4
6,5,5,13,7,8,5
1,7,4,5,16,8,3
10,8,8,5,12,13,10

Page 85
9,16,6,4,3,6,10
3,9,9,6,8,6,9
14,6,2,9,18,16,9
8,9,3,12,3,7,5
3,5,8,9,6,3,13
13,9,8,9,3,6,5
8,6,3,5,8,8,9
3,8,9,13,8,9,5

Page 86
9,6,7,3,3,3,4
2,3,5,6,9,5,2
5,7,3,3,4,9,3
2,7,9,4,5,3,9
6,16,3,9,9,12,17
3,7,5,13,9,9,6
9,15,7,18,9,3,9
5,9,9,6,5,14,7

Page 87
8,2,8,7,4,14,9
0,3,5,7,8,6,8
3,6,2,3,12,9,4
0,6,2,16,2,4,4
14,1,4,9,4,1,8
8,6,8,1,3,10,10
4,1,9,8,18,4,6
7,10,1,8,1,6,5

Page 88
7,3,4,5,7,3,2
5,2,7,4,3,5,3
3,7,2,3,5,4,2
2,13,1,5,4,13,1
7,8,5,3,8,1,8
1,3,5,8,5,3,5
5,1,7,4,13,8,1
13,3,8,1,3,2,3

Page 89
3,4,5,2
10,3,7,3
9,5,4,9
7,2,3,5
6,4,3,3
2,7,5,4
7,2,9,3,5,3,4
3,9,5,2,9,3,2
9,7,4,9,3,7,4
2,3,9,3,7,4,5

Page 90
7,9,2,16,6,13,4
5,17,3,3,5,2,8
3,16,14,7,7,8,3
14,15,3,4,4,5,11
4,3,7,8
3,10,8,4
4,7,4,6
7,8,10,4
6,8,3,6
2,3,7,4
7,8,6,4

Page 91
6,9,6,10,9,3,2
0,3,8,2,8,9,6
9,4,7,8,9,3,0
6,9,6,6,10,8,4
8,6,4,6,7,5,9
6,10,4,8,14,6,2
12,7,3,10,16,8,10
8,9,8,6,5,3,4

Page 92
5,9,6,8,5,7,4
8,7,5,9,8,9,5
7,10,9,8,9,6,7
8,9,10,7,5,7,2
9,5,6,8,10,16,8
10,8,9,5,7,7,5
9,9,3,7,10,5,8
7,5,10,2,8,8,14

Page 93
13,8,8,4,13,8,6
10,5,8,8,5,3,13
5,6,5,2,8,6,13
8,13,8,8,10,3,10
8,3,9,4,8,12,5
6,13,10,5,14,5,8
8,3,8,13,8,2,3
6,5,16,8,7,9,5

Page 94
13,8,5,2,5,3,8
3,3,4,13,8,13,5
5,3,13,2,4,3,3
8,3,8,13,2,5,4
5,7,5,9,13,8,7
9,8,3,10,8,8,5
4,13,9,7,3,5,9
13,5,8,5,6,13,5

Page 95
10,12,6,14,6,10,6
10,8,8,14,9,9,13
9,9,16,10,17,7,11
13,12,13,7,8,15,5
7,4,3,8,3,2,5
7,8,3,3,1,6,6
9,4,8,4,5,0,3
2,1,8,5,1,6,9

Page 96
10,5,9,1,4,9,6
10,16,4,6,8,7,5
16,8,8,7,6,0,12
4,5,4,13,2,9,10
13,5,9,1
9,13,3,8
5,17,8,6
3,6,6,9
9,8,7,8
1,15,3,3

Name _____

TRICK   <u>Rhymes</u> or <u>Count by 3s</u>

Say: Three, six, nine! Who do you think is mighty fine?

3   6   9

Learn
$$\begin{array}{r} 3 \\ +\,6 \\ \hline 9 \end{array} \qquad \begin{array}{r} 6 \\ +\,3 \\ \hline 9 \end{array} \qquad \begin{array}{r} 9 \\ -\,3 \\ \hline 6 \end{array} \qquad \begin{array}{r} 9 \\ -\,6 \\ \hline 3 \end{array}$$

$$\begin{array}{r} 3 \\ +\,6 \\ \hline 9 \end{array} \quad \begin{array}{r} 6 \\ +\,3 \\ \hline \end{array} \quad \begin{array}{r} 3 \\ +\, \\ \hline 9 \end{array} \quad \begin{array}{r} 3 \\ +\,6 \\ \hline \end{array} \quad \begin{array}{r} 9 \\ -\,3 \\ \hline \end{array} \quad \begin{array}{r} 3 \\ +\, \\ \hline 9 \end{array} \quad \begin{array}{r} 3 \\ +\,6 \\ \hline \end{array}$$

$$\begin{array}{r} 6 \\ +\,3 \\ \hline \end{array} \quad \begin{array}{r} 6 \\ +\, \\ \hline 9 \end{array} \quad \begin{array}{r} 9 \\ -\,6 \\ \hline \end{array} \quad \begin{array}{r} 6 \\ +\,3 \\ \hline \end{array} \quad \begin{array}{r} 9 \\ -\,6 \\ \hline \end{array} \quad \begin{array}{r} 9 \\ -\,3 \\ \hline \end{array} \quad \begin{array}{r} 6 \\ +\,3 \\ \hline \end{array}$$

Practice **Count by 3s**, **Number +1**, and **Backwards 1**.

$$\begin{array}{r} 9 \\ -\,3 \\ \hline \end{array} \quad \begin{array}{r} 1 \\ +\,2 \\ \hline \end{array} \quad \begin{array}{r} 3 \\ +\,6 \\ \hline \end{array} \quad \begin{array}{r} 8 \\ -\,1 \\ \hline \end{array} \quad \begin{array}{r} 6 \\ +\,3 \\ \hline \end{array} \quad \begin{array}{r} 9 \\ +\,1 \\ \hline \end{array} \quad \begin{array}{r} 9 \\ -\,6 \\ \hline \end{array}$$

$$\begin{array}{r} 3 \\ -\,1 \\ \hline \end{array} \quad \begin{array}{r} 10 \\ -\,1 \\ \hline \end{array} \quad \begin{array}{r} 9 \\ -\,6 \\ \hline \end{array} \quad \begin{array}{r} 9 \\ -\,1 \\ \hline \end{array} \quad \begin{array}{r} 4 \\ +\,1 \\ \hline \end{array} \quad \begin{array}{r} 4 \\ -\,1 \\ \hline \end{array} \quad \begin{array}{r} 3 \\ +\,6 \\ \hline \end{array}$$

$$\begin{array}{r} 9 \\ -\,6 \\ \hline \end{array} \quad \begin{array}{r} 9 \\ -\,3 \\ \hline \end{array} \quad \begin{array}{r} 1 \\ +\,6 \\ \hline \end{array} \quad \begin{array}{r} 6 \\ +\,3 \\ \hline \end{array} \quad \begin{array}{r} 5 \\ -\,1 \\ \hline \end{array} \quad \begin{array}{r} 9 \\ -\,3 \\ \hline \end{array} \quad \begin{array}{r} 7 \\ +\,1 \\ \hline \end{array}$$

$$\begin{array}{r} 3 \\ +\,6 \\ \hline \end{array} \quad \begin{array}{r} 1 \\ +\,3 \\ \hline \end{array} \quad \begin{array}{r} 6 \\ +\,3 \\ \hline \end{array} \quad \begin{array}{r} 9 \\ -\,6 \\ \hline \end{array} \quad \begin{array}{r} 1 \\ +\,7 \\ \hline \end{array} \quad \begin{array}{r} 5 \\ +\,1 \\ \hline \end{array} \quad \begin{array}{r} 1 \\ +\,8 \\ \hline \end{array}$$

Two Plus Two Is Not Five, Easy Methods To Learn Addition and Subtraction   **57**

Name _____

Practice **Count by 3s** and **Zero**.

9 − 3	6 + 3	5 − 0	3 + 6	0 + 4	4 − 4	9 − 6
3 + 6	7 + 0	2 − 2	6 + 3	9 − 3	0 + 5	3 + 6
3 + 0	9 − 6	0 + 8	9 − 3	5 − 5	6 + 3	9 − 0
9 − 6	6 − 6	3 + 6	3 + 0	6 + 3	9 − 3	9 − 9

Practice **Count by 3s** and **Right Next to Each Other**.

3 + 6	9 − 3	9 − 8	9 − 6	6 + 3	5 − 4	6 + 3
9 − 6	8 − 7	3 − 2	9 − 3	3 + 6	7 − 6	9 − 6
10 − 9	6 + 3	9 − 3	6 − 5	9 − 6	4 − 3	3 + 6
2 − 1	9 − 3	7 − 6	3 + 6	9 − 8	6 + 3	8 − 7

Two Plus Two Is Not Five, Easy Methods To Learn Addition and Subtraction

Name _____

Practice **Count by 3s** and **Number in the Middle**.

6 + 3	3 + 6	9 − 3	3 + 5	2 + 4	9 − 6	5 + 3
6 + 4	9 − 6	5 + 3	4 + 2	4 + 6	3 + 6	9 − 3
3 + 6	3 + 5	6 + 4	9 − 3	6 + 3	9 − 6	4 + 6
4 + 2	6 + 3	5 + 3	9 − 6	3 + 5	3 + 6	2 + 4

Practice **Count by 3s** and **Magic 9**.

6 + 3	9 + 2	9 − 6	5 + 9	9 − 3	9 + 3	4 + 9
9 − 3	3 + 9	3 + 6	9 + 6	9 + 4	9 − 6	6 + 3
9 + 8	9 − 3	9 + 9	6 + 3	7 + 9	2 + 9	3 + 6
3 + 6	6 + 9	9 − 6	9 + 5	8 + 9	9 − 3	9 + 7

Two Plus Two Is Not Five, Easy Methods To Learn Addition and Subtraction

Name _____

Cumulative Practice. (Circle) **Count by 3s**.

9 − 3	12 − 6	3 + 6	7 + 7	8 + 2	6 + 1	9 + 6
1 − 1	2 + 4	5 − 1	2 + 6	9 − 6	1 + 5	3 + 4
6 + 6	4 + 9	5 + 3	7 − 6	3 + 6	9 + 9	9 − 6
6 + 2	6 + 4	2 + 3	6 + 3	6 + 0	10 − 5	4 − 3
7 + 1	6 − 5	9 − 3	9 + 8	9 − 9	3 + 5	2 + 8
2 − 0	8 + 1	9 − 8	9 − 6	3 + 2	14 − 7	0 + 4
3 + 9	6 + 3	8 − 4	4 + 6	2 + 9	4 + 3	9 − 3

Two Plus Two Is Not Five, Easy Methods To Learn Addition and Subtraction

Name _____

TRICK   Learn more with Doubles.

8 + 8 **16**	8 + 8	4 + 4	8 + 8	5 + 5	2 + 2	8 + 8

1 + 1	7 + 7	8 + 8	3 + 3	6 + 6	8 + 8	7 + 7

Learn **Doubles Subtraction**.

16 − 8 **8**	8 + 8	8 + ___ 16	16 − 8	8 + 8	8 + ___ 16	16 − 8

Practice **Doubles**.

16 − 8	7 + 7	16 − 8	14 − 7	8 + 8	10 − 5	6 − 3

8 + 8	16 − 8	8 + 8	12 − 6	16 − 8	4 − 2	8 + 8

14 − 7	6 + 6	7 + 7	16 − 8	5 + 5	8 + 8	16 − 8

16 − 8	8 − 4	2 + 2	8 + 8	6 − 3	16 − 8	12 − 6

Two Plus Two Is Not Five, Easy Methods To Learn Addition and Subtraction   **61**

Name _____

Practice **Doubles** and **Number in the Middle**.

8 + 8	16 − 8	12 − 6	5 + 3	6 + 4	7 + 7	14 − 7
4 + 4	3 + 5	8 + 8	7 + 7	16 − 8	4 + 6	8 − 4
10 − 5	16 − 8	6 + 4	14 − 7	12 − 6	6 − 3	3 + 5
5 + 3	8 + 8	6 + 6	4 + 6	7 + 7	2 + 2	16 − 8
14 − 7	5 + 5	4 − 2	8 + 8	6 + 4	5 + 3	3 + 3

Practice **Doubles** and **Zero** this way.

10−5= _____   8+8= _____   8−4= _____   5−5= _____

4+4= _____   7+7= _____   9−0= _____   0+8= _____

16−8= _____   12−6= _____   5+5= _____   3+0= _____

14−7= _____   3−3= _____   4−2= _____   6−3= _____

8+8= _____   4+0= _____   16−8= _____   2−0= _____

Name _____

TRICK Learn more <u>Doubles Subtraction.</u>

You know 9 + 9 = 18. (Magic 9)   Learn **18 − 9 = 9**.

18 **− 9** **9**	9 + 9	9 + __ 18	18 − 9	2 + 2	18 − 9	8 + 8
9 + 9	9 + __ 18	18 − 9	9 + 9	9 + __ 18	6 + 6	9 + 9
18 −__ 9	18 − 9	10 − 5	18 − 9	4 + 4	18 − 9	7 + 7
9 + 9	14 − 7	18 − 9	5 + 5	18 − 9	12 − 6	8 + 8
16 − 8	18 − 9	3 + 3	8 − 4	14 − 7	18 − 9	16 − 8

Practice **Doubles** this way.

18−9= _____   8+8= _____   9+9= _____   16−8= _____

8−4= _____   7+7= _____   6+6= _____   4+4= _____

6−3= _____   14−7= _____   16−8= _____   18−9= _____

10−5= _____   18−9= _____   12−6= _____   8+8= _____

Two Plus Two Is Not Five, Easy Methods To Learn Addition and Subtraction   **63**

TIER 3

Name _____

Practice **Doubles**, **Backwards 1**, and **Number +1**.

18 − 9	7 − 1	10 − 5	1 + 4	9 + 9	10 − 1	16 − 8
3 + 1	6 − 1	18 − 9	7 + 7	6 + 6	1 + 9	14 − 7
9 − 1	8 + 8	1 + 2	18 − 9	8 + 1	9 + 9	6 + 1

Cumulative Practice.

2 + 6	18 − 9	5 − 1	3 + 5	9 + 8	5 − 0	4 + 3
16 − 8	1 + 6	12 − 6	5 + 0	7 + 7	9 − 8	9 + 2
3 + 2	4 + 2	18 − 9	8 + 8	16 − 8	6 + 2	9 + 9
8 − 4	4 + 9	3 + 4	5 + 1	2 + 3	4 + 4	1 − 1
8 + 2	8 + 8	5 − 4	5 + 5	6 + 4	7 + 1	14 − 7

Two Plus Two Is Not Five, Easy Methods To Learn Addition and Subtraction

Name _____

TRICK   Family Partners

You know   2   and   3   Learn   **5**   **5**
           $+\,3$ $+\,2$ $-\,3$ $-\,2$
           $\overline{5}$ $\overline{5}$ $\overline{2}$ $\overline{3}$

Look at   **5**   This **Looks Like** Number in the Middle.
          $\underset{....}{}$
          $-\,3$
              $\longleftarrow$ So the answer = 2

Look at   **5–2**.

What number is missing from the family?

$$2 + \underline{\quad\quad} = 5$$

Practice these. Mark — **Looks Like Number in the Middle.**

2	5	5	3	5	2	5
$+\,3$	$-\,3$	$-\,2$	$+\,2$	$-\,3$	$+\,3$	$-\,2$

5	5	2	5	3	5	2
$+\,1$	$-\,2$	$+\,3$	$-\,3$	$+\,2$	$-\,2$	$+\,0$

5	4	5	2	5	3	5
$-\,3$	$-\,1$	$-\,3$	$+\,3$	$-\,2$	$+\,2$	$-\,3$

2	5	3	0	2	5	5
$+\,2$	$-\,2$	$+\,2$	$+\,3$	$+\,3$	$-\,3$	$-\,2$

Two Plus Two Is Not Five, Easy Methods To Learn Addition and Subtraction   **65**

Name _____

Practice **Number Family 2•3•5**, **Magic 9**, and **Backwards 1**.

5 − 2	9 + 9	6 − 1	6 + 9	5 − 3	8 − 1	9 + 8
7 − 1	5 − 2	4 − 1	9 + 7	2 + 3	5 + 9	5 − 1
5 − 3	9 + 2	10 − 1	5 − 2	9 + 6	2 + 3	5 − 2
4 + 9	9 − 1	5 − 2	3 + 9	5 − 3	8 + 9	3 − 1

Practice **Number Family** and **Right Next to Each Other**.

3 + 2	8 − 7	5 − 2	10 − 9	5 − 3	3 − 2	6 − 5
5 − 3	2 + 3	7 − 6	9 − 8	2 + 3	5 − 4	2 − 1
10 − 9	5 − 2	3 + 2	3 − 2	4 − 3	3 + 2	5 − 2
5 − 3	7 − 6	5 − 2	8 − 7	5 − 3	6 − 5	2 + 3

Two Plus Two Is Not Five, Easy Methods To Learn Addition and Subtraction

Name _____

Practice **Number Family** and **Number in the Middle**.

3 + 2	5 − 3	4 + 6	5 − 2	2 + 4	6 + 4	5 + 3
5 − 2	3 + 5	5 − 3	2 + 3	3 + 5	5 − 2	6 + 4
4 + 6	3 + 2	5 + 3	5 − 3	4 + 6	2 + 4	3 + 5
4 + 2	5 − 2	6 + 4	2 + 3	2 + 4	5 + 3	5 − 3

Practice **Number Family**, **Number +1**, and **Zero**.

5 − 3	3 + 2	8 − 0	5 − 2	1 + 8	2 + 3	6 + 1
9 + 0	2 + 3	5 − 5	9 + 1	5 − 3	0 + 4	5 − 2
3 + 2	4 + 1	5 − 2	3 + 1	1 + 7	6 − 6	5 − 3
0 + 3	1 + 6	2 + 3	5 − 2	1 − 1	3 + 2	4 − 0

Two Plus Two Is Not Five, Easy Methods To Learn Addition and Subtraction

Name _____

Cumulative Practice. (Circle) **Number Family**.

9 + 3	2 + 3	6 + 4	7 − 7	5 − 3	3 + 1	8 − 7
5 − 2	10 − 1	2 + 6	5 + 3	6 − 3	3 + 2	5 − 3
8 +2	5 − 3	12 − 6	5 − 2	6 + 9	4 + 6	2 + 3
5 − 3	4 + 3	2 + 4	3 + 2	4 − 2	5 − 2	10 − 9
2 + 3	5 − 3	3 + 4	7 + 7	3 + 5	2 + 1	3 + 2
8 + 2	6 + 4	1 + 8	3 + 0	5 − 3	4 + 9	2 + 8
5 − 2	14 − 7	6 + 2	5 + 3	9 + 5	5 − 2	4 − 3

Two Plus Two Is Not Five, Easy Methods To Learn Addition and Subtraction

Name _____

TRICK   2 Ladder Subtraction

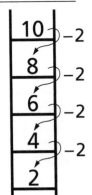

Count down by 2-steps.

What is on the step below?

<u>10</u>   <u>8</u   <u>4</u   <u>10</u   <u>6</u   <u>8</u   <u>4</u   <u>6</u

___   ___   ___   ___   ___   ___   ___   ___

Try **2 Ladder Subtraction**.

10	8	10	6	10	8	6
− 2	− 2	− 2	− 2	− 2	− 2	− 2

8	4	6	10	8	6	4
− 2	− 2	− 2	− 2	− 2	− 2	− 2

↑ (This is also <u>Doubles Subtraction</u>.)

Practice **2 Ladder**.

6	10	8	8	6	2	10
+ 2	− 2	+ 2	− 2	− 2	+ 6	− 2

6	2	2	6	4	8	6
− 2	+ 4	+ 8	− 2	+ 2	− 2	+ 2

2	10	2	8	4	6	8
+ 2	− 2	+ 6	− 2	− 2	− 2	− 2

Two Plus Two Is Not Five, Easy Methods To Learn Addition and Subtraction   **69**

Name _____

Practice going up a 2-step and down a 2-step.

8 ↓ □   □ ↑ 4   □ ↑ 8   10 ↓ □

4 ↓ □   6 ↓ □   10 ↓ □   □ ↑ 6

□ ↑ 8   □ ↑ 4   8 ↓ □   6 ↓ □

Practice.

10 − 2	8 − 2	4 + 2	10 − 2	6 + 2	8 + 2	6 − 2
2 + 8	8 − 7	6 − 2	8 − 2	4 − 2	2 + 6	8 + 2
8 − 2	6 + 2	2 + 8	4 + 4	6 − 2	8 − 2	10 − 2
6 − 2	2 + 4	10 − 2	8 + 2	3 + 1	3 + 3	4 + 2

Two Plus Two Is Not Five, Easy Methods To Learn Addition and Subtraction

Name _____

Practice **2 Ladder** and **Magic 9**. (Circle) **2 Ladder**.

2 + 6	9 + 6	8 − 2	4 + 9	8 + 2	10 − 2	6 − 2
2 + 4	2 + 9	9 + 9	8 − 2	7 + 9	6 + 2	5 + 9
10 − 2	9 + 8	2 + 8	4 − 2	6 + 2	9 + 4	8 − 2
6 − 2	8 + 2	6 + 9	6 − 2	9 + 3	10 − 2	2 + 6

Practice **2 Ladder** and **Zero**.

4 + 2	10 − 2	6 − 0	2 + 8	3 − 3	0 + 1	2 + 6
6 − 2	7 + 0	2 + 4	6 − 2	8 + 2	4 − 0	8 − 2
10 − 2	4 − 2	0 + 8	6 + 2	10 − 2	6 − 2	5 − 0
9 − 9	2 + 4	2 + 8	8 − 2	2 + 0	2 + 6	8 − 2

Two Plus Two Is Not Five, Easy Methods To Learn Addition and Subtraction 71

Name _____

Practice **2 Ladder** and **Right Next to Each Other**.

$\begin{array}{r} 2 \\ +8 \\ \hline \end{array}$	$\begin{array}{r} 7 \\ -6 \\ \hline \end{array}$	$\begin{array}{r} 6 \\ -2 \\ \hline \end{array}$	$\begin{array}{r} 10 \\ -2 \\ \hline \end{array}$	$\begin{array}{r} 4 \\ +2 \\ \hline \end{array}$	$\begin{array}{r} 10 \\ -9 \\ \hline \end{array}$	$\begin{array}{r} 2 \\ +6 \\ \hline \end{array}$
$\begin{array}{r} 3 \\ -2 \\ \hline \end{array}$	$\begin{array}{r} 6 \\ +2 \\ \hline \end{array}$	$\begin{array}{r} 2 \\ +4 \\ \hline \end{array}$	$\begin{array}{r} 9 \\ -8 \\ \hline \end{array}$	$\begin{array}{r} 8 \\ +2 \\ \hline \end{array}$	$\begin{array}{r} 2 \\ -1 \\ \hline \end{array}$	$\begin{array}{r} 8 \\ -2 \\ \hline \end{array}$
$\begin{array}{r} 10 \\ -2 \\ \hline \end{array}$	$\begin{array}{r} 4 \\ -2 \\ \hline \end{array}$	$\begin{array}{r} 5 \\ -4 \\ \hline \end{array}$	$\begin{array}{r} 2 \\ +6 \\ \hline \end{array}$	$\begin{array}{r} 4 \\ -3 \\ \hline \end{array}$	$\begin{array}{r} 2 \\ +8 \\ \hline \end{array}$	$\begin{array}{r} 8 \\ -7 \\ \hline \end{array}$
$\begin{array}{r} 6 \\ +2 \\ \hline \end{array}$	$\begin{array}{r} 10 \\ -9 \\ \hline \end{array}$	$\begin{array}{r} 8 \\ -2 \\ \hline \end{array}$	$\begin{array}{r} 2 \\ +4 \\ \hline \end{array}$	$\begin{array}{r} 6 \\ -5 \\ \hline \end{array}$	$\begin{array}{r} 4 \\ -2 \\ \hline \end{array}$	$\begin{array}{r} 6 \\ -2 \\ \hline \end{array}$

Practice **2 Ladder** and **Number in the Middle**.

$\begin{array}{r} 8 \\ +2 \\ \hline \end{array}$	$\begin{array}{r} 5 \\ +3 \\ \hline \end{array}$	$\begin{array}{r} 6 \\ -2 \\ \hline \end{array}$	$\begin{array}{r} 10 \\ -2 \\ \hline \end{array}$	$\begin{array}{r} 2 \\ +6 \\ \hline \end{array}$	$\begin{array}{r} 4 \\ +6 \\ \hline \end{array}$	$\begin{array}{r} 8 \\ -2 \\ \hline \end{array}$
$\begin{array}{r} 4 \\ +6 \\ \hline \end{array}$	$\begin{array}{r} 4 \\ +2 \\ \hline \end{array}$	$\begin{array}{r} 4 \\ -2 \\ \hline \end{array}$	$\begin{array}{r} 3 \\ +5 \\ \hline \end{array}$	$\begin{array}{r} 8 \\ -2 \\ \hline \end{array}$	$\begin{array}{r} 2 \\ +8 \\ \hline \end{array}$	$\begin{array}{r} 5 \\ +3 \\ \hline \end{array}$
$\begin{array}{r} 8 \\ -2 \\ \hline \end{array}$	$\begin{array}{r} 3 \\ +5 \\ \hline \end{array}$	$\begin{array}{r} 10 \\ -2 \\ \hline \end{array}$	$\begin{array}{r} 6 \\ +4 \\ \hline \end{array}$	$\begin{array}{r} 6 \\ +2 \\ \hline \end{array}$	$\begin{array}{r} 4 \\ +6 \\ \hline \end{array}$	$\begin{array}{r} 6 \\ -2 \\ \hline \end{array}$
$\begin{array}{r} 6 \\ +4 \\ \hline \end{array}$	$\begin{array}{r} 2 \\ +4 \\ \hline \end{array}$	$\begin{array}{r} 5 \\ +3 \\ \hline \end{array}$	$\begin{array}{r} 2 \\ +8 \\ \hline \end{array}$	$\begin{array}{r} 3 \\ +5 \\ \hline \end{array}$	$\begin{array}{r} 6 \\ +2 \\ \hline \end{array}$	$\begin{array}{r} 10 \\ -2 \\ \hline \end{array}$

Name _____

TRICK Double +1   Looks like <u>Right Next to Each Other.</u>

Double the lesser number and add 1.

$$\begin{array}{r}④\\+5\\\hline9\end{array}\qquad\begin{array}{r}4\\+4\\\hline8\\+1\end{array}\;\square\;+1\text{ more}\;\blacksquare=\begin{array}{r}4\\+5\\\hline9\end{array}$$

LOOK. These are the same.

$$\begin{array}{r}④\\+5\\\hline9\end{array}\quad\begin{array}{r}5\\+④\\\hline9\end{array}\qquad\begin{array}{r}5\\+4\end{array}\quad\begin{array}{r}4\\+5\end{array}\quad\begin{array}{r}4\\+4\end{array}\quad\begin{array}{r}4\\+5\end{array}\quad\begin{array}{r}5\\+4\end{array}$$

Practice these. Mark) **Double +1**.

$$\begin{array}{r}4\\+4\end{array}\quad\begin{array}{r}4\\+5\end{array}\!)\quad\begin{array}{r}2\\+2\end{array}\quad\begin{array}{r}2\\+3\end{array}\!)\quad\begin{array}{r}5\\+4\end{array}\quad\begin{array}{r}4\\+5\end{array}\quad\begin{array}{r}4\\+3\end{array}$$

$$\begin{array}{r}3\\+3\end{array}\quad\begin{array}{r}3\\+4\end{array}\quad\begin{array}{r}5\\+4\end{array}\quad\begin{array}{r}4\\+5\end{array}\quad\begin{array}{r}1\\+1\end{array}\quad\begin{array}{r}5\\+4\end{array}\quad\begin{array}{r}3\\+2\end{array}$$

$$\begin{array}{r}2\\+2\end{array}\quad\begin{array}{r}4\\+5\end{array}\quad\begin{array}{r}6\\-5\end{array}\quad\begin{array}{r}5\\+4\end{array}\quad\begin{array}{r}10\\-5\end{array}\quad\begin{array}{r}4\\+3\end{array}\quad\begin{array}{r}6\\+6\end{array}$$

$$\begin{array}{r}3\\+4\end{array}\quad\begin{array}{r}6\\-3\end{array}\quad\begin{array}{r}4\\+5\end{array}\quad\begin{array}{r}12\\-6\end{array}\quad\begin{array}{r}3\\+2\end{array}\quad\begin{array}{r}0\\+5\end{array}\quad\begin{array}{r}4\\+5\end{array}$$

$$\begin{array}{r}8\\-7\end{array}\quad\begin{array}{r}5\\+4\end{array}\quad\begin{array}{r}3\\+2\end{array}\quad\begin{array}{r}4\\+5\end{array}\quad\begin{array}{r}3\\+4\end{array}\quad\begin{array}{r}10\\-1\end{array}\quad\begin{array}{r}9\\-9\end{array}$$

Two Plus Two Is Not Five, Easy Methods To Learn Addition and Subtraction   **73**

Name _____

Practice **Double +1**, **Number +1**, and **Backwards 1**.

5	4	3	7	3	6	4
+ 4	+ 1	+ 2	− 1	+ 4	+ 1	+ 3

1	10	4	3	5	4	1
+ 8	− 1	+ 3	+ 1	− 1	+ 5	+ 9

3	5	4	2	1	4	3
+ 4	+ 4	− 1	+ 3	+ 2	+ 5	+ 2

7	2	4	1	3	9	5
+ 1	+ 3	+ 5	+ 5	+ 2	− 1	+ 4

Practice **Double +1** and **Magic 9** this way.

2+3= _____   9+5= _____   4+3= _____   3+9= _____

9+2= _____   5+4= _____   6+9= _____   3+4= _____

4+5= _____   4+9= _____   7+9= _____   2+3= _____

8+9= _____   3+2= _____   5+4= _____   9+7= _____

4+3= _____   9+9= _____   9+8= _____   4+5= _____

9+6= _____   5+4= _____   3+2= _____   5+9= _____

Name _____

Practice **Double +1** and **Right Next to Each Other**.

3	6	2	4	5	5	4
+ 4	− 5	+ 3	− 3	+ 4	− 4	+ 5

4	10	5	3	7	3	2
+ 3	− 9	+ 4	+ 2	− 6	+ 4	+ 3

3	5	4	9	3	4	8
− 2	− 4	+ 3	− 8	+ 4	+ 5	− 7

3	5	4	6	2	4	3
+ 2	+ 4	+ 5	− 5	+ 3	− 3	+ 2

Practice **Double +1**, **Number in the Middle**, and **Zero** this way.

4+5= _____	3+5= _____	3+0= _____	4+3= _____
5−5= _____	3+2= _____	3+4= _____	4+6= _____
3−3= _____	5+4= _____	5+3= _____	2−2= _____
2+3= _____	3+4= _____	0−0= _____	4+6= _____
4+5= _____	6+4= _____	0+8= _____	5+4= _____
6−0= _____	4+3= _____	3+5= _____	9+0= _____

Two Plus Two Is Not Five, Easy Methods To Learn Addition and Subtraction **75**

Name _____

Cumulative Practice.

1	9	3	6	14	3	7
+ 6	+ 4	+ 5	− 6	− 7	+ 2	− 6

0	6	3	9	6	2	5
+ 8	− 3	+ 4	− 1	+ 4	+ 8	+ 4

2	6	4	4	7	5	7
+ 9	+ 2	+ 1	+ 5	+ 9	+ 3	− 0

4	3	4	8	2	6	4
+ 6	− 2	+ 2	+ 2	+ 3	+ 6	+ 3

3	9	1	0	4	4	9
+ 2	+ 5	+ 7	+ 2	− 3	+ 3	+ 1

8	4	3	3	9	7	9
+ 0	+ 5	+ 3	− 1	+ 6	+ 0	− 8

12	3	5	1	4	4	2
− 6	+ 4	+ 4	+ 9	+ 0	+ 5	+ 6

4	5	1	3	4	7	8
− 1	+ 4	− 0	+ 9	+ 4	+ 7	− 8

Name _____

TRICK   Family Partners

You know   3   and   4   Learn   7   7
           + 4   + 3   − 3   − 4
           ———   ———   ———   ———
             7   7   4   3

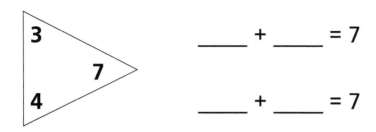

____ + ____ = 7

____ + ____ = 7

What number is missing from the family?

3 + _____ = 7   4 + _____ = 7

Practice.

3	3	7	4	4	7	7
+ 4	+	− 3	+ 3	+	− 4	− 3
	7			7		

7	4	4	7	7	2	3
− 4	+	+ 4	− 3	− 4	+ 1	+
	7					7

8	3	7	1	7	5	7
− 1	+ 4	−	+ 9	− 3	+ 5	− 4
		3				

| 4 | 4 | 7 | 7 | 0 | 7 | 3 |
| + 3 | + 0 | − 4 | − 7 | + 1 | − 3 | + 4 |

Name _____

Practice **Number Family 3•4•7** and **Zero**.

3	7	2	7	0	4	6
+ 4	− 3	− 2	− 4	+ 4	+ 3	+ 0

7	8	4	9	5	7	3
− 4	− 8	+ 3	− 0	+ 0	− 3	+ 4

4	7	0	7	7	3	3
+ 3	− 0	+ 3	− 4	− 3	+ 4	− 3

0	7	4	4	3	5	7
+ 1	− 3	+ 3	− 0	+ 4	− 0	− 4

Practice **Number Family** and **Number in the Middle**.

4+3= _____   7−4= _____   4+6= _____   7−3= _____

5+3= _____   3+5= _____   7−3= _____   4+3= _____

7−3= _____   6+4= _____   3+5= _____   7−4= _____

6+4= _____   7−3= _____   4+6= _____   3+4= _____

7−4= _____   3+4= _____   7−3= _____   5+3= _____

2+4= _____   4+6= _____   3+5= _____   7−4= _____

Name _____

Practice **Number Family** and **Magic 9**.

4+3= _____	9+5= _____	3+4= _____	7−3= _____
9+6= _____	4+9= _____	7−4= _____	9+9= _____
3+9= _____	7−3= _____	5+9= _____	9+3= _____
3+4= _____	9+2= _____	4+3= _____	7−4= _____
8+9= _____	9+7= _____	7−3= _____	3+4= _____
7−4= _____	4+3= _____	6+9= _____	7−3= _____
9+4= _____	7−4= _____	7+9= _____	9+8= _____

Practice **Number Family**, **Backwards 1**, and **Right Next to Each Other**.

7 − 3	9 − 8	4 − 1	7 − 4	3 − 2	4 + 3	10 − 1
8 − 7	7 − 4	4 − 3	3 + 4	7 − 3	9 − 1	5 − 4
3 + 4	6 − 1	7 − 4	10 − 9	2 − 1	3 + 4	7 − 4
5 − 1	7 − 3	7 − 1	8 − 1	6 − 5	7 − 3	4 + 3

Two Plus Two Is Not Five, Easy Methods To Learn Addition and Subtraction **79**

Name _____

Cumulative Practice. (Circle) **Family Partners**.

3 + 4	6 + 2	9 + 9	2 − 1	4 + 3	7 − 3	12 − 6

7 − 4	2 + 8	5 + 9	5 + 3	7 − 4	6 + 6	6 − 6

9 + 2	4 + 3	7 + 7	7 − 3	2 + 9	2 + 6	2 + 3

7 − 6	7 − 4	4 + 2	4 + 6	3 + 3	8 − 4	3 + 5

3 + 4	4 − 3	6 + 6	4 + 9	7 − 3	9 + 7	5 − 4

0 + 9	6 + 4	7 − 3	4 − 0	4 + 4	8 + 2	4 + 3

14 − 7	3 + 2	3 + 4	1 + 6	6 − 3	7 − 4	6 + 9

Two Plus Two Is Not Five, Easy Methods To Learn Addition and Subtraction

Name _____

TRICK Curvy Numbers

LOOK. **3 · S · 8** have curves that look the same.

3   **S**   **8**

Curvy **3** + Curvy **5** = Curvy **8**   Curvy **8** − Curvy **3** = Curvy **5**
Curvy **5** + Curvy **3** = Curvy **8**   Curvy **8** − Curvy **5** = Curvy **3**

$$\begin{array}{r} 3 \\ +\,5 \\ \hline 8 \end{array} \qquad \begin{array}{r} 5 \\ +\,3 \\ \hline 8 \end{array} \qquad\qquad \begin{array}{r} 8 \\ -\,3 \\ \hline 5 \end{array} \qquad \begin{array}{r} 8 \\ -\,5 \\ \hline 3 \end{array}$$

(These are also <u>Number in the Middle</u>.)

Curvy **5** + Curvy **8** = Curvy **13**   Curvy **13** − Curvy **5** = Curvy **8**
Curvy **8** + Curvy **5** = Curvy **13**   Curvy **13** − Curvy **8** = Curvy **5**

$$\begin{array}{r} 5 \\ +\,8 \\ \hline 13 \end{array} \qquad \begin{array}{r} 8 \\ +\,5 \\ \hline 13 \end{array} \qquad\qquad \begin{array}{r} 13 \\ -\,5 \\ \hline 8 \end{array} \qquad \begin{array}{r} 13 \\ -\,8 \\ \hline 5 \end{array}$$

Practice **Curvy Numbers**.

$$\begin{array}{r} 3 \\ +\,5 \\ \hline \end{array} \quad \begin{array}{r} 5 \\ +\,8 \\ \hline \end{array} \quad \begin{array}{r} 8 \\ -\,5 \\ \hline \end{array} \quad \begin{array}{r} 5 \\ +\,3 \\ \hline \end{array} \quad \begin{array}{r} 8 \\ +\,5 \\ \hline \end{array} \quad \begin{array}{r} 8 \\ +\, \\ \hline 13 \end{array} \quad \begin{array}{r} 13 \\ -\,8 \\ \hline \end{array}$$

$$\begin{array}{r} 5 \\ +\,8 \\ \hline \end{array} \quad \begin{array}{r} 5 \\ +\, \\ \hline 13 \end{array} \quad \begin{array}{r} 13 \\ -\,5 \\ \hline \end{array} \quad \begin{array}{r} 13 \\ -\,8 \\ \hline \end{array} \quad \begin{array}{r} 5 \\ +\,3 \\ \hline \end{array} \quad \begin{array}{r} 5 \\ +\,8 \\ \hline \end{array} \quad \begin{array}{r} 8 \\ -\,5 \\ \hline \end{array}$$

$$\begin{array}{r} 8 \\ -\,3 \\ \hline \end{array} \quad \begin{array}{r} 13 \\ -\,5 \\ \hline \end{array} \quad \begin{array}{r} 13 \\ -\,8 \\ \hline \end{array} \quad \begin{array}{r} 8 \\ -\,5 \\ \hline \end{array} \quad \begin{array}{r} 8 \\ +\,5 \\ \hline \end{array} \quad \begin{array}{r} 13 \\ -\,5 \\ \hline \end{array} \quad \begin{array}{r} 8 \\ -\,3 \\ \hline \end{array}$$

Two Plus Two Is Not Five, Easy Methods To Learn Addition and Subtraction

Name _____

Practice **Curvy Numbers** and **Zero**. Circle **Curvy Numbers**.

13	8	5	5	3	8	9
− 5	+ 0	− 5	+ 8	+ 5	− 3	+ 0

5	13	0	8	13	8	8
+ 3	− 8	+ 3	− 5	− 8	− 0	− 5

5	5	8	3	8	5	13
− 0	+ 8	− 3	− 0	+ 5	+ 3	− 5

8	3	13	8	8	8	8
− 3	− 3	− 5	+ 5	− 8	− 5	+ 5

Practice **Curvy Numbers** and **Right Next to Each Other**.

8	9	5	7	13	6	5
+ 5	− 8	+ 3	− 6	− 8	− 5	+ 8

4	8	13	5	8	8	8
− 3	− 3	− 5	+ 8	− 5	+ 5	− 3

10	5	8	8	13	8	5
− 9	+ 3	+ 5	− 7	− 8	− 5	− 4

5	13	8	3	3	13	8
+ 8	− 5	− 3	+ 5	− 2	− 8	− 5

Two Plus Two Is Not Five, Easy Methods To Learn Addition and Subtraction

Name _____

Practice **Curvy Numbers** and **Magic 9**.

8 − 3	9 + 5	13 − 5	5 + 3	13 − 8	8 + 9	4 + 9
9 + 8	8 − 5	8 + 5	9 + 4	9 + 2	5 + 8	3 + 5
3 + 9	13 − 8	2 + 9	5 + 9	8 + 5	8 − 5	9 + 6
5 + 8	5 + 3	6 + 9	8 − 3	9 + 7	3 + 5	13 − 5

Practice **Curvy Numbers** and **Backwards 1**.

13−8= _____   7−1= _____   10−1= _____   8−3= _____

5−1= _____   8+5= _____   13−8= _____   6−1= _____

8−5= _____   9−1= _____   2−1= _____   8−5= _____

4−1= _____   13−5= _____   5+8= _____   8−1= _____

13−5= _____   3−1= _____   8−3= _____   5+3= _____

8+5= _____   8−5= _____   5−1= _____   5+8= _____

8−3= _____   3+5= _____   8−5= _____   10−1= _____

Two Plus Two Is Not Five, Easy Methods To Learn Addition and Subtraction

Name _____

Practice **Curvy Numbers** and **Number in the Middle**.

5 + 8	6 + 4	5 + 3	8 + 5	4 + 6	8 − 3	13 − 8
3 + 5	4 + 2	13 − 8	6 + 4	13 − 5	5 + 3	8 − 5
13 − 5	5 + 8	2 + 4	8 − 3	8 + 5	4 + 6	13 − 5

Cumulative Practice.

6 − 6	13 − 5	3 + 4	8 + 2	8 + 5	2 − 0	4 + 6
5 + 8	13 − 8	9 + 3	8 − 5	7 + 7	4 − 3	8 − 4
12 − 6	4 + 1	8 − 3	8 + 5	8 − 1	13 − 5	3 + 2
6 − 5	14 − 7	4 + 0	13 − 8	7 + 9	3 + 5	8 − 5
6 + 4	5 + 3	6 + 2	8 − 3	6 + 6	5 + 8	2 + 8

Name _____

Tiers 1, 2, and 3 Review
Review **Count by 3s** and **Doubles**.

6 + 3	8 + 8	9 − 3	8 − 4	9 − 6	12 − 6	5 + 5
9 − 6	3 + 6	6 + 3	3 + 3	16 − 8	9 − 3	6 + 3
7 + 7	9 − 3	4 − 2	6 + 3	9 + 9	8 + 8	3 + 6
4 + 4	18 − 9	9 − 6	6 + 6	6 − 3	14 − 7	10 − 5

Review **Count by 3s** and **Curvy Numbers**.

9 − 6	13 − 8	3 + 5	6 + 3	9 − 3	9 − 6	5 + 8
8 + 5	3 + 6	13 − 5	3 + 6	8 − 5	9 − 3	13 − 8
5 + 3	9 − 3	8 − 5	8 − 3	13 − 5	3 + 5	6 + 3
9 − 6	13 − 5	6 + 3	5 + 8	5 + 3	3 + 6	8 − 3

Two Plus Two Is Not Five, Easy Methods To Learn Addition and Subtraction **85**

Name _____

Tiers 1, 2, and 3 Review
Review **Count by 3s** and **Number Families**.

3 + 6	9 − 3	3 + 4	9 − 6	7 − 4	5 − 2	7 − 3
5 − 3	7 − 4	3 + 2	9 − 3	6 + 3	2 + 3	5 − 3
2 + 3	4 + 3	9 − 6	5 − 2	7 − 3	3 + 6	9 − 6
5 − 3	3 + 4	3 + 6	7 − 3	3 + 2	5 − 2	6 + 3

Review **Count by 3s**, **Magic 9**, and **Double +1**.

9 − 3	9 + 7	9 − 6	5 + 4	6 + 3	3 + 9	9 + 8
9 − 6	3 + 4	2 + 3	4 + 9	4 + 5	3 + 6	9 − 3
3 + 6	6 + 9	4 + 3	9 + 9	6 + 3	9 − 6	5 + 4
3 + 2	6 + 3	4 + 5	9 − 3	2 + 3	9 + 5	3 + 4

Name _____

Tiers 1, 2, and 3 Review
Review **Doubles**, **Number Families**, and **Zero**.

4 + 4	5 − 3	16 − 8	3 + 4	7 − 3	7 + 7	9 − 0
9 − 9	7 − 4	2 + 3	4 + 3	8 + 0	3 + 3	16 − 8
5 − 2	6 − 0	1 + 1	7 − 4	6 + 6	18 − 9	8 − 4
8 − 8	12 − 6	5 − 3	8 + 8	4 − 2	7 − 3	0 + 4

Review **Doubles**, **Right Next to Each Other**, and **2 Ladder**.

7 + 7	7 − 6	6 − 2	18 − 9	8 − 4	4 − 3	10 − 2
16 − 8	8 − 2	2 + 6	8 − 7	6 − 3	8 + 2	5 + 5
2 + 2	5 − 4	18 − 9	10 − 2	9 + 9	6 − 2	12 − 6
14 − 7	2 + 8	10 − 9	6 + 2	6 − 5	4 + 2	10 − 5

Two Plus Two Is Not Five, Easy Methods To Learn Addition and Subtraction **87**

Name _____

Tiers 1, 2, and 3 Review
Review **Number Families**.

3 + 4	5 − 2	7 − 3	2 + 3	4 + 3	7 − 4	5 − 3
2 + 3	5 − 3	3 + 4	7 − 3	5 − 2	3 + 2	7 − 4
5 − 2	4 + 3	5 − 3	7 − 4	3 + 2	7 − 3	5 − 3

Review **Number Families**, **Curvy Numbers**, and **Right Next to Each Other**.

5 − 3	5 + 8	7 − 6	13 − 8	7 − 3	8 + 5	9 − 8
4 + 3	13 − 5	8 − 3	5 − 2	3 + 5	5 − 4	5 + 3
6 − 5	8 − 5	2 + 3	5 + 3	13 − 8	7 − 4	8 − 3
3 + 2	8 − 7	3 + 4	7 − 3	5 + 8	3 + 5	4 − 3
8 + 5	5 − 2	13 − 5	3 − 2	8 − 5	5 − 3	7 − 4

Two Plus Two Is Not Five, Easy Methods To Learn Addition and Subtraction

Name _____

Tiers 1, 2, and 3 Review
Review **Number Families**, **Backwards 1**, and **Number +1** this way.

5−2= _____   7−3= _____   4+1= _____   5−3= _____

9+1= _____   1+2= _____   3+4= _____   7−4= _____

10−1= _____   3+2= _____   1+3= _____   1+8= _____

4+3= _____   5−3= _____   7−4= _____   2+3= _____

5+1= _____   7−3= _____   5−2= _____   4−1= _____

5−3= _____   8−1= _____   6−1= _____   7−3= _____

Review **Number Families** and **Double +1**.

$$\begin{array}{ccccccc}
3 & 5 & 5 & 7 & 3 & 5 & 7 \\
+4 & -3 & +4 & -4 & +2 & -2 & -3 \\
\end{array}$$

$$\begin{array}{ccccccc}
5 & 4 & 2 & 5 & 5 & 7 & 5 \\
-2 & +5 & +3 & -3 & +4 & -4 & -3 \\
\end{array}$$

$$\begin{array}{ccccccc}
5 & 4 & 7 & 4 & 7 & 3 & 7 \\
+4 & +3 & -3 & +5 & -4 & +4 & -3 \\
\end{array}$$

$$\begin{array}{ccccccc}
5 & 7 & 4 & 5 & 3 & 7 & 2 \\
-3 & -4 & +5 & -2 & +4 & -3 & +3 \\
\end{array}$$

Two Plus Two Is Not Five, Easy Methods To Learn Addition and Subtraction   **89**

Name _____

Tiers 1, 2, and 3 Review
Review **Number Families**, **Doubles**, and **Magic 9**.

$$\begin{array}{r} 4 \\ +\ 3 \\ \hline \end{array} \qquad \begin{array}{r} 18 \\ -\ 9 \\ \hline \end{array} \qquad \begin{array}{r} 5 \\ -\ 3 \\ \hline \end{array} \qquad \begin{array}{r} 9 \\ +\ 7 \\ \hline \end{array} \qquad \begin{array}{r} 12 \\ -\ 6 \\ \hline \end{array} \qquad \begin{array}{r} 4 \\ +\ 9 \\ \hline \end{array} \qquad \begin{array}{r} 7 \\ -\ 3 \\ \hline \end{array}$$

$$\begin{array}{r} 3 \\ +\ 2 \\ \hline \end{array} \qquad \begin{array}{r} 8 \\ +\ 9 \\ \hline \end{array} \qquad \begin{array}{r} 6 \\ -\ 3 \\ \hline \end{array} \qquad \begin{array}{r} 7 \\ -\ 4 \\ \hline \end{array} \qquad \begin{array}{r} 2 \\ +\ 3 \\ \hline \end{array} \qquad \begin{array}{r} 5 \\ -\ 3 \\ \hline \end{array} \qquad \begin{array}{r} 4 \\ +\ 4 \\ \hline \end{array}$$

$$\begin{array}{r} 7 \\ -\ 4 \\ \hline \end{array} \qquad \begin{array}{r} 8 \\ +\ 8 \\ \hline \end{array} \qquad \begin{array}{r} 9 \\ +\ 5 \\ \hline \end{array} \qquad \begin{array}{r} 14 \\ -\ 7 \\ \hline \end{array} \qquad \begin{array}{r} 3 \\ +\ 4 \\ \hline \end{array} \qquad \begin{array}{r} 16 \\ -\ 8 \\ \hline \end{array} \qquad \begin{array}{r} 5 \\ -\ 2 \\ \hline \end{array}$$

$$\begin{array}{r} 7 \\ +\ 7 \\ \hline \end{array} \qquad \begin{array}{r} 6 \\ +\ 9 \\ \hline \end{array} \qquad \begin{array}{r} 5 \\ -\ 2 \\ \hline \end{array} \qquad \begin{array}{r} 7 \\ -\ 3 \\ \hline \end{array} \qquad \begin{array}{r} 8 \\ -\ 4 \\ \hline \end{array} \qquad \begin{array}{r} 10 \\ -\ 5 \\ \hline \end{array} \qquad \begin{array}{r} 9 \\ +\ 2 \\ \hline \end{array}$$

Review **Number Family 3•4•7** and **2 Ladder** this way.

7−3= _____	7−4= _____	4+3= _____	10−2= _____
7−4= _____	8+2= _____	6+2= _____	7−3= _____
6−2= _____	3+4= _____	7−3= _____	2+4= _____
4+3= _____	2+6= _____	2+8= _____	7−3= _____
8−2= _____	10−2= _____	7−4= _____	4+2= _____
4−2= _____	7−4= _____	3+4= _____	6−2= _____
3+4= _____	6+2= _____	8−2= _____	7−3= _____

Name _____

Tiers 1, 2, and 3 Review

Review **2 Ladder**, **Count by 3s**, and **Zero**.

2 + 4	6 + 3	9 − 3	8 + 2	3 + 6	9 − 6	0 + 2
9 − 9	9 − 6	2 + 6	4 − 2	8 − 0	3 + 6	9 − 3
3 + 6	6 − 2	7 − 0	10 − 2	6 + 3	9 − 6	6 − 6
8 − 2	6 + 3	4 + 2	9 − 3	2 + 8	6 + 2	4 + 0

Review **2 Ladder**, **Doubles**, and **Backwards 1**.

2 + 6	12 − 6	5 − 1	4 + 2	14 − 7	10 − 5	18 − 9
3 + 3	8 + 2	6 − 2	9 − 1	7 + 7	8 − 2	4 − 2
6 + 6	8 − 1	4 − 1	2 + 8	8 + 8	6 + 2	5 + 5
16 − 8	18 − 9	10 − 2	7 − 1	6 − 1	6 − 3	8 − 4

Two Plus Two Is Not Five, Easy Methods To Learn Addition and Subtraction **91**

Name _____

Tiers 1, 2, and 3 Review
Review **Double +1** and **2 Ladder**.

2 + 3	4 + 5	8 − 2	6 + 2	3 + 2	3 + 4	6 − 2
10 − 2	4 + 3	3 + 2	5 + 4	2 + 6	4 + 5	2 + 3
3 + 4	8 + 2	4 + 5	10 − 2	5 + 4	2 + 4	4 + 3
6 + 2	5 + 4	2 + 8	4 + 3	2 + 3	3 + 4	4 − 2

Review **Double +1**, **Number in the Middle**, and **Doubles**.

5 + 4	2 + 3	12 − 6	4 + 4	6 + 4	8 + 8	5 + 3
4 + 6	3 + 5	4 + 5	10 − 5	4 + 3	14 − 7	3 + 2
18 − 9	5 + 4	6 − 3	3 + 4	4 + 6	3 + 2	3 + 5
4 + 3	2 + 3	6 + 4	1 + 1	16 − 8	5 + 3	7 + 7

Two Plus Two Is Not Five, Easy Methods To Learn Addition and Subtraction

Name _____

Tiers 1, 2, and 3 Review
Review **Curvy Numbers** and **2 Ladder**.

5 + 8	6 + 2	10 − 2	6 − 2	8 + 5	13 − 5	4 + 2
2 + 8	13 − 8	5 + 3	2 + 6	8 − 3	8 − 5	5 + 8
13 − 8	8 − 2	8 − 3	4 − 2	2 + 6	8 − 2	8 + 5
10 − 2	5 + 8	3 + 5	13 − 5	2 + 8	8 − 5	8 + 2

Review **Curvy Numbers** and **Doubles**.

13 − 5	8 − 5	18 − 9	8 − 4	5 + 3	6 + 6	10 − 5
3 + 3	5 + 8	5 + 5	13 − 8	7 + 7	8 − 3	4 + 4
3 + 5	6 − 3	16 − 8	5 + 8	13 − 5	1 + 1	8 − 5
12 − 6	8 − 3	8 + 8	5 + 3	14 − 7	18 − 9	13 − 8

Two Plus Two Is Not Five, Easy Methods To Learn Addition and Subtraction **93**

Name _____

Tiers 1, 2, and 3 Review
Review **Curvy Numbers**, **Family Partners 2•3•5** and **3•4•7**.

5 + 8	3 + 5	13 − 8	5 − 3	8 − 3	7 − 4	13 − 5
7 − 4	5 − 2	7 − 3	8 + 5	13 − 5	5 + 8	8 − 3
13 − 8	8 − 5	8 + 5	5 − 3	7 − 3	8 − 5	5 − 2
5 + 3	7 − 4	13 − 5	5 + 8	5 − 3	13 − 8	7 − 3

Review **Curvy Numbers**, **Double +1**, and **Number +1**.

8 − 3	6 + 1	13 − 8	4 + 5	8 + 5	13 − 5	3 + 4
5 + 4	5 + 3	1 + 2	9 + 1	13 − 5	1 + 7	2 + 3
3 + 1	5 + 8	5 + 4	4 + 3	8 − 5	13 − 8	1 + 8
8 + 5	3 + 2	13 − 5	2 + 3	1 + 5	5 + 8	4 + 1

Name _____

Tiers 1, 2, and 3 Review
Review addition.

8	3	4	7	5	6	0
+ 2	+ 9	+ 2	+ 7	+ 1	+ 4	+ 6

5	3	6	9	6	4	8
+ 5	+ 5	+ 2	+ 5	+ 3	+ 5	+ 5

3	5	8	2	9	3	9
+ 6	+ 4	+ 8	+ 8	+ 8	+ 4	+ 2

4	6	5	1	4	6	2
+ 9	+ 6	+ 8	+ 6	+ 4	+ 9	+ 3

Review subtraction.

8	6	8	16	6	4	13
− 1	− 2	− 5	− 8	− 3	− 2	− 8

14	9	5	9	8	12	8
− 7	− 1	− 2	− 6	− 7	− 6	− 2

9	7	10	8	8	1	7
− 0	− 3	− 2	− 4	− 3	− 1	− 4

5	5	13	10	7	9	18
− 3	− 4	− 5	− 5	− 6	− 3	− 9

Name _____

Tiers 1, 2, and 3 Review
Review all tricks.

8 + 2	13 − 8	3 + 6	10 − 9	1 + 3	4 + 5	12 − 6

4 + 6	8 + 8	6 − 2	9 − 3	2 + 6	4 + 3	8 − 3

7 + 9	10 − 2	5 + 3	14 − 7	2 + 4	2 − 2	9 + 3

7 − 3	5 − 0	8 − 4	5 + 8	5 − 3	18 − 9	6 + 4

8+5= _____   3+2= _____   5+4= _____   6−5= _____

8+1= _____   9+4= _____   8−5= _____   3+5= _____

10−5= _____   8+9= _____   16−8= _____   4+2= _____

7−4= _____   3+3= _____   8−2= _____   6+3= _____

10−1= _____   8−0= _____   3+4= _____   13−5= _____

9−8= _____   9+6= _____   5−2= _____   9−6= _____

Two Plus Two Is Not Five, Easy Methods To Learn Addition and Subtraction

Tier 4

Instructions and Information

Start with any trick. The tricks may be introduced in any order except:

- All the **Big Subtraction** sets of facts should be taught in the given sequence, but each set does not immediately have to follow the set before it.

Page	Trick	Math fact cards to be assigned:
97-100	**Straight Lines**	4+7, 7+4, 11-4, 11-7
101-104	**Family Partners**	9-4, 9-5
105-108	**Number in the Middle**	5+7, 7+5, 6+8, 8+6
109-110	**Big Subtraction**	17-8, 17-9
111-112	**Big Subtraction**	16-7, 16-9
113-115	**Big Subtraction**	15-6, 15-9
116-117	**Big Subtraction**	14-5, 14-9
118-119	**Big Subtraction**	13-4, 13-9
120-121	**Big Subtraction**	12-3, 12-9
122-124	**Big Subtraction**	11-2, 11-9
125-134	**Review Pages**	

Tier 4 Answers

Page 97
11,11,7,11,4,7,11
11,7,1,1,4,11,4
1,4,11,7,1,1,11

Page 98
11,7,4,9,6,3,7
9,6,11,3,9,4,11
3,4,9,7,11,6,11
7,9,3,6,11,9,4
11,12,5,3,4,7,8
8,6,11,4,7,14,7
4,2,9,11,6,11,2
6,11,4,10,7,16,11

Page 99
7,11,4,7,6,0,11
0,9,11,4,5,4,2
11,7,5,3,7,9,11
6,4,10,6,11,2,7
4,11,2,11,5,12,16
17,3,13,7,18,5,11
15,7,2,5,11,14,4
11,12,13,3,18,11,11

Page 100
11,5,10,4,9,7,9
3,11,5,7,15,5,4
4,5,6,8,6,11,10
8,3,11,1,4,6,7
3,11,4,7,14,4,8
4,1,13,12,3,7,11
4,7,11,8,11,7,8
9,9,8,2,11,16,3

Page 101
4,5, or 5,4
5,4
9,9,5,5,4,4,5
5,9,4,8,5,5,7
4,4,4,5,1,5,4
8,5,9,4,5,0,9

Page 102
5,10,8,9,6,5,4
9,4,6,4,4,8,5
4,8,5,6,8,5,9
10,9,5,4,6,4,4
9,5,7,9
4,7,4,7
9,3,5,4
3,9,7,4
4,9,4,5
7,5,3,4

Page 103
9,4,17,5,4,7,5
13,9,5,4,16,4,9
5,12,6,10,18,5,4
15,9,4,14,9,11,8
5,9,8,4,3,13,5
9,8,5,5,13,8,5
13,5,3,5,8,4,8
8,9,13,4,5,9,5

Page 104
9,9,4,3,7,5,4
6,3,13,4,3,13,6
4,9,2,16,5,16,5
5,4,0,10,1,3,9
4,5,8,2,3,7,4
8,5,9,17
12,8,5,7
5,2,10,8
3,13,8,4
8,10,6,9
14,6,9,5

Page 105
5,8,7,6
7,4,6,8
5,7,6,8,7,6
12,14,16

Page 106
14,12,8,12,16,8,14
16,6,14,10,12,10,16
12,10,16,8,14,8,10
12,14,6,12,9,8,3
16,6,9,14,12,6,10
9,14,16,10,9,8,3

Page 107
12,6,6,8,8,4,16
14,10,8,16,14,10,12
16,8,6,4,14,10,10
8,12,2,14,12,8,2
10,13,4,7,12,15,8
14,7,11,17,3,14,7
3,10,6,14,18,7,12
12,12,16,8,14,4,8

Page 108
14,12,9,8,7,5,10
9,14,7,16,12,14,7
16,9,5,12,10,8,14
12,8,16,2,5,5,14
5,8,3,13,12,2,8
10,12,3,5,5,14,12
16,3,14,12,10,5,5
2,14,8,3,13,12,14

Page 109
9,9,8,9,10,9,8
4,8,9,5,9,8,9
9,9,6,9,8,9,9

Page 110
9,9,6,9,9,8,9
4,8,9,7,9,8,2
9,9,5,8,9,3,9
8,1,9,9,8,9,9
9,8,8,8,9,4,8
6,9,10,9,2,8,8
8,9,8,6,9,10,9
6,9,4,9,6,8,6

Page 111
9,8,7,6,9,9,8
9,7,14,9,9,8,10
7,9,9,4,8,9,9
9,9,8,7,6,9,7

Page 112
9,1,9,7,1,7,1
8,7,9,1,8,9,9
1,1,9,1,1,9,8
9,1,7,9,9,1,7
7,5,9,9,9,8,3
8,9,9,13,7,6,3
8,9,3,5,9,9,9
6,13,7,8,9,8,9

Page 113
9,6,9,8,6,9,9
8,7,9,9,2,6,4
6,9,12,7,9,8,7
9,9,9,6,14,7,9

Page 114
6,7,9,7,9,5,9
9,9,9,7,9,7,7
5,8,9,9,5,6,9
9,9,7,9,5,8,6
8,9,7,9
9,9,9,6
9,6,7,8
9,9,9,9
8,9,7,6
9,9,6,9

Page 115
9,12,16,6,7,9,4
8,8,9,9,6,6,7
7,9,18,8,5,9,9
10,9,6,9,8,6,6
7,17,6,3
13,5,1,10
8,9,6,0
3,7,7,10
5,9,9,16
9,8,14,4
6,9,13,9

Page 116
5,9,7,9,5,8,9
9,6,18,7,9,5,9
9,9,8,5,14,6,5
9,9,6,16,7,9,9

Page 117
9,9,9,0,9,9,5
9,5,3,0,9,8,5
0,8,7,9,6,9,4
5,6,7,9,0,3,7
6,9,9,4,5,9,7
3,2,9,8,5,7,3
8,3,9,6,9,9,5
7,5,6,3,2,9,5

Page 118
9,7,4,6,9,5,4
9,8,9,9,9,10,9
4,12,6,9,9,7,9
9,9,9,9,5,4,9

Page 119
4,13,8,7,4,9,3
9,9,13,6,5,9,8
3,5,9,9,13,4,8
9,13,5,5,5,8,9
9,7,7,8
7,9,9,9
9,5,4,9
5,10,9,9
8,6,9,4
7,3,4,5
4,5,9,9

Page 120
3,9,9,9,4,3,9
8,9,9,9,8,9,3
5,7,3,6,9,9,5
9,6,4,9,3,9,4

Page 121
9,8,8,4,7,6,3
9,4,10,3,3,6,6
12,5,5,4,14,9,9
9,9,16,3,9,9,2
9,3,0,2,5,9,9
9,3,5,6,7,6,1
9,18,3,3
13,9,8,9
9,10,4,3

Page 122
2,9,9,4,2,9,8
9,7,2,6,9,9,5
9,2,9,9,3,4,9
9,3,9,9,9,9,2

Page 123
2,8,3,9
8,9,10,7
6,9,6,4
2,9,8,9
5,8,4,2
6,10,9,9
9,9,6,8
9,12,9,2
9,4,18,9
15,9,2,14
2,9,13,3
14,9,9,16
8,11,17,9

Page 124
2,7,6,5,10,3,14
9,1,9,2,13,10,9
9,5,9,9,9,8,8
4,9,7,5,9,9,12
2,6,9,5
14,10,9,1
9,8,4,5
5,9,7,0
10,3,6,2
8,4,15,9
3,9,9,6

Page 125
11,9,4,5,7,11,4
7,7,11,9,5,7,11
7,11,7,4,11,9,7
11,7,9,11,7,5,4
11,10,7,11,6,4,6
7,4,11,10,11,8,7
8,11,2,11,6,11,8
7,11,6,4,8,4,11

Page 126
7,11,9,9,8,4,6
3,7,11,9,4,2,7
4,9,9,11,9,7,11
9,11,9,4,11,5,4
11,8,4,8,5,13,11
7,5,13,5,3,11,8
13,8,11,7,8,3,5
11,5,5,8,4,8,13

Page 127
9,14,10,4,5,10,12
16,4,14,8,16,5,9
10,9,12,5,14,12,14
8,6,4,14,9,5,12
9,5,12,4,7,10,9
5,16,6,4,5,18,2
6,7,4,9,9,5,4
9,2,8,5,3,4,8

Page 128
4,9,2,9,9,9,9
4,9,9,0,5,3,4
6,2,9,5,9,9,4
5,4,7,8,5,5,0
5,9,7,4,7,11,4
3,11,5,7,2,5,4
9,4,11,3,7,7,4
4,4,9,11,3,5,2

Page 129
14,6,6,8,8,4,8
12,1,8,16,14,10,12
5,8,6,10,8,4,10
8,9,14,2,12,4,10
12,14,1,13
1,10,16,1
15,1,10,12
1,12,8,1
11,1,15,14
8,16,12,1
18,14,6,17

Page 130
12,9,4,14,6,6,9
9,12,14,5,9,10,3
6,9,9,12,3,14,5
14,10,16,4,8,9,12
14,7,12,8
10,8,13,4
5,11,5,10
12,7,8,11
3,13,11,6
14,12,8,14
4,5,12,3

Page 131
5,9,4,9,4,9,9
7,3,5,4,9,9,5
5,7,9,6,5,8,9
7,9,9,4,2,7,5
2,13,9,8,9,3,13
9,5,9,8,3,5,9
8,9,13,6,9,9,5
7,5,4,9,5,3,8

Page 132
3,14,2,7,9,8,12
9,4,10,6,14,9,5
12,9,9,10,9,9,14
6,12,16,9,8,16,9
6,9,11,7
9,4,2,8
7,9,11,4
7,9,9,11
3,9,4,5
11,9,9,7
4,9,11,3

Page 133
8,17,5,9,7,9,14
7,10,13,5,8,8,9
12,6,10,9,5,14,11
5,8,9,0,5,4,3
9,4,12,2,4,7,3
4,4,8,1,3,9,12
7,3,8,14,9,3,15
16,5,3,1,6,13,11

Page 134
6,5,9,2,3,9,6
10,8,18,7,14,6,1
4,8,13,16,6,7,8
5,11,9,8,5,3,12
4,6,10,9
9,9,11,13
5,14,8,2
7,4,0,1
5,10,12,5
7,3,12,11
9,14,3,9

Name _____

TRICK Straight Lines

Look.

1 2 3 **4** 5 6 **7** 8 9

Numerals **1**, **4**, and **7** are very straight.

Very straight	**4**		Very straight	**7**	
+ very straight	**+ 7**		+ very straight	**+ 4**	
= very straight	**11**		= very straight	**11**	

So,

Very straight	**11**		Very straight	**11**
– very straight	**– 4**		– very straight	**– 7**
= very straight	**7**		= very straight	**4**

Try.

7	4	11	7	11	11	4
+ 4	**+ 7**	**– 4**	**+ 4**	**– 7**	**– 4**	**+ 7**

Practice **Straight Lines** and **Right Next to Each Other**.

4	11	4	8	11	7	11
+ 7	**– 4**	**– 3**	**– 7**	**– 7**	**+ 4**	**– 7**

3	11	4	11	10	7	7
– 2	**– 7**	**+ 7**	**– 4**	**– 9**	**– 6**	**+ 4**

Name _____

Practice **Straight Lines** and **Count by 3s**.

7 + 4	11 − 4	11 − 7	3 + 6	9 − 3	9 − 6	11 − 4
6 + 3	9 − 3	4 + 7	9 − 6	3 + 6	11 − 7	7 + 4
9 − 6	11 − 7	6 + 3	11 − 4	4 + 7	9 − 3	4 + 7
11 − 4	3 + 6	9 − 6	9 − 3	7 + 4	6 + 3	11 − 7

Practice **Straight Lines** and **Doubles**.

4 + 7	6 + 6	10 − 5	6 − 3	11 − 7	11 − 4	4 + 4
16 − 8	12 − 6	7 + 4	8 − 4	11 − 4	7 + 7	14 − 7
11 − 7	4 − 2	18 − 9	7 + 4	3 + 3	4 + 7	1 + 1
12 − 6	7 + 4	11 − 7	5 + 5	11 − 4	8 + 8	4 + 7

Two Plus Two Is Not Five, Easy Methods To Learn Addition and Subtraction

Name _____

Practice **Straight Lines**, **Backwards 1**, **Number +1**, and **Zero**.

11	4	11	1	7	3	4
− 4	+ 7	− 7	+ 6	− 1	− 3	+ 7

8	0	7	3	6	11	2
− 8	+ 9	+ 4	+ 1	− 1	− 7	+ 0

7	8	5	4	11	1	4
+ 4	− 1	− 0	− 1	− 4	+ 8	+ 7

1	11	9	0	7	2	11
+ 5	− 7	+ 1	+ 6	+ 4	− 0	− 4

Practice **Straight Lines**, **Magic 9**, and **Number Family 2•3•5**.

11	2	5	7	2	3	9
− 7	+ 9	− 3	+ 4	+ 3	+ 9	+ 7

8	5	9	11	9	3	7
+ 9	− 2	+ 4	− 4	+ 9	+ 2	+ 4

9	11	5	2	4	5	11
+ 6	− 4	− 3	+ 3	+ 7	+ 9	− 7

4	9	4	5	9	7	9
+ 7	+ 3	+ 9	− 2	+ 9	+ 4	+ 2

Two Plus Two Is Not Five, Easy Methods To Learn Addition and Subtraction **99**

Name _____

Cumulative Practice. (Circle) **Straight Lines**.

7 + 4	0 + 5	2 + 8	6 − 2	4 + 5	11 − 4	6 + 3
5 − 2	4 + 7	3 + 2	11 − 4	9 + 6	13 − 8	11 − 7
11 − 7	10 − 5	9 − 3	5 + 3	12 − 6	4 + 7	6 + 4
4 + 4	6 − 3	7 + 4	6 − 5	11 − 7	8 − 2	11 − 4
9 − 6	7 + 4	5 − 1	11 − 4	7 + 7	11 − 7	16 − 8
11 − 7	9 − 8	8 + 5	6 + 6	8 − 5	4 + 3	7 + 4
7 − 3	14 − 7	4 + 7	1 + 7	2 + 9	11 − 4	8 − 0
5 + 4	3 + 6	10 − 2	5 − 3	7 + 4	8 + 8	7 − 4

Two Plus Two Is Not Five, Easy Methods To Learn Addition and Subtraction

Name _____

TRICK   Family Partners

You know   4   and   5   Learn   9   9
           + 5   + 4   − 5   − 4
           ———   ———   ———   ———
            9   9   4   5

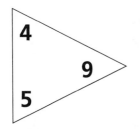

_____ + _____ = 9

_____ + _____ = 9

What number is missing from the family?

4 + _____ = 9   5 + _____ = 9

Practice.

5	4	4	9	5	9	9
+ 4	+ 5	+ ___	− 4	+ ___	− 5	− 4
		9		9		

9	5	9	4	9	4	6
− 4	+ 4	− 5	+ 4	− 4	+ ___	+ 1
					9	

5	9	8	4	2	9	9
+ ___	− 5	− 4	+ ___	− 1	− 4	− 5
9			9			

4	9	5	9	9	9	4
+ 4	− 4	+ 4	− 5	− 4	− 9	+ 5

Two Plus Two Is Not Five, Easy Methods To Learn Addition and Subtraction

TIER 4

Name _____

Practice **Number Family 4•5•9** and **2 Ladder**.

9 − 4	2 + 8	10 − 2	5 + 4	8 − 2	9 − 4	9 − 5
4 + 5	9 − 5	4 + 2	9 − 5	6 − 2	6 + 2	9 − 4
9 − 5	2 + 6	9 − 4	8 − 2	10 − 2	9 − 4	4 + 5
8 + 2	5 + 4	9 − 4	9 − 5	2 + 4	6 − 2	9 − 5

Practice **Number Families 4•5•9** and **3•4•7**.

4+5= _____	9−4= _____	3+4= _____	5+4= _____
7−3= _____	4+3= _____	9−5= _____	4+3= _____
5+4= _____	7−4= _____	9−4= _____	9−5= _____
7−4= _____	4+5= _____	3+4= _____	7−3= _____
9−5= _____	5+4= _____	7−3= _____	9−4= _____
3+4= _____	9−4= _____	7−4= _____	9−5= _____

Two Plus Two Is Not Five, Easy Methods To Learn Addition and Subtraction

Name _____

Practice **Number Family 4•5•9**, **Number +1**, and **Magic 9**.

4 + 5	9 − 5	9 + 8	9 − 4	1 + 3	6 + 1	9 − 4
9 + 4	5 + 4	9 − 4	3 + 1	7 + 9	9 − 5	5 + 4
9 − 4	3 + 9	1 + 5	1 + 9	9 + 9	4 + 1	9 − 5
9 + 6	8 + 1	9 − 5	5 + 9	4 + 5	9 + 2	7 + 1

Practice **Number Family** and **Curvy Numbers**.

9 − 4	4 + 5	3 + 5	9 − 5	8 − 5	5 + 8	13 − 8
5 + 4	5 + 3	8 − 3	9 − 4	8 + 5	13 − 5	8 − 3
8 + 5	13 − 8	8 − 5	13 − 8	3 + 5	9 − 5	5 + 3
13 − 5	5 + 4	5 + 8	9 − 5	8 − 3	4 + 5	9 − 4

Two Plus Two Is Not Five, Easy Methods To Learn Addition and Subtraction

Name _____

Cumulative Practice.

5 + 4	18 − 9	9 − 5	1 + 2	4 + 3	2 + 3	7 − 3
4 + 2	6 − 3	5 + 8	6 − 2	9 − 6	9 + 4	0 + 6
8 − 4	3 + 6	5 − 3	7 + 9	8 − 3	8 + 8	9 − 4
3 + 2	9 − 5	8 − 8	6 + 4	3 − 2	5 − 2	4 + 5
7 − 3	9 − 4	10 − 2	5 − 3	7 − 4	14 − 7	9 − 5

3+5= _____   10−5= _____   5+4= _____   9+8= _____

6+6= _____   2+6= _____   2+3= _____   3+4= _____

9−4= _____   4−2= _____   2+8= _____   13−5= _____

5−2= _____   8+5= _____   16−8= _____   9−5= _____

9−1= _____   4+6= _____   8−2= _____   6+3= _____

7+7= _____   9−3= _____   4+5= _____   9−4= _____

Two Plus Two Is Not Five, Easy Methods To Learn Addition and Subtraction

Name _____

TRICK Number in the Middle with Doubles

What fits in the middle?

4 _____ 6   7 _____ 9   8 _____ 6   5 _____ 7

6 _____ 8   5 _____ 3   7 _____ 5   9 _____ 7

LOOK. This is the same.

6	8	5	9	6	7
◯	◯	◯	◯	◯	◯
4	6	7	7	8	5

Learn **Number in the Middle** with **Doubles**.

5 _____ 7

$\begin{array}{r} 5 \\ \cdots \\ +7 \\ \hline 12 \end{array}$ ⟶ 6 fits in the middle.

$\begin{array}{r} 5 \\ +7 \\ \hline 12 \end{array}$

5+1
7−1

Double 6.
$\begin{array}{r} 6 \\ +6 \\ \hline \end{array}$

6 _____ 8

$\begin{array}{r} 6 \\ \cdots \\ +8 \\ \hline 14 \end{array}$ ⟶ 7 fits in the middle.

$\begin{array}{r} 6 \\ +8 \\ \hline 14 \end{array}$

6+1
8−1

Double 7.
$\begin{array}{r} 7 \\ +7 \\ \hline \end{array}$

7 _____ 9

$\begin{array}{r} 7 \\ \cdots \\ +9 \\ \hline 16 \end{array}$ ⟶ 8 fits in the middle.

$\begin{array}{r} 7 \\ +9 \\ \hline 16 \end{array}$

7+1
9−1

Double 8.
$\begin{array}{r} 8 \\ +8 \\ \hline \end{array}$

↑ (This is also <u>Magic 9</u>.)

Two Plus Two Is Not Five, Easy Methods To Learn Addition and Subtraction

Name _____

Look. These are the same.

$$\begin{array}{r} 8 \\ + 6 \\ \hline 14 \end{array} \;{}^{7+7}$$ $$\begin{array}{r} 9 \\ + 7 \\ \hline 16 \end{array} \;{}^{8+8}$$ $$\begin{array}{r} 7 \\ + 5 \\ \hline 12 \end{array} \;{}^{6+6}$$

Practice **Number in the Middle**.

$$\begin{array}{r} 6 \\ + 8 \\ \hline \end{array} \quad \begin{array}{r} 7 \\ + 5 \\ \hline \end{array} \quad \begin{array}{r} 3 \\ + 5 \\ \hline \end{array} \quad \begin{array}{r} 5 \\ + 7 \\ \hline \end{array} \quad \begin{array}{r} 7 \\ + 9 \\ \hline \end{array} \quad \begin{array}{r} 5 \\ + 3 \\ \hline \end{array} \quad \begin{array}{r} 8 \\ + 6 \\ \hline \end{array}$$

$$\begin{array}{r} 9 \\ + 7 \\ \hline \end{array} \quad \begin{array}{r} 2 \\ + 4 \\ \hline \end{array} \quad \begin{array}{r} 6 \\ + 8 \\ \hline \end{array} \quad \begin{array}{r} 4 \\ + 6 \\ \hline \end{array} \quad \begin{array}{r} 5 \\ + 7 \\ \hline \end{array} \quad \begin{array}{r} 6 \\ + 4 \\ \hline \end{array} \quad \begin{array}{r} 9 \\ + 7 \\ \hline \end{array}$$

$$\begin{array}{r} 7 \\ + 5 \\ \hline \end{array} \quad \begin{array}{r} 4 \\ + 6 \\ \hline \end{array} \quad \begin{array}{r} 7 \\ + 9 \\ \hline \end{array} \quad \begin{array}{r} 5 \\ + 3 \\ \hline \end{array} \quad \begin{array}{r} 8 \\ + 6 \\ \hline \end{array} \quad \begin{array}{r} 3 \\ + 5 \\ \hline \end{array} \quad \begin{array}{r} 6 \\ + 4 \\ \hline \end{array}$$

Practice **Number in the Middle** and **Count by 3s**.

$$\begin{array}{r} 5 \\ + 7 \\ \hline \end{array} \quad \begin{array}{r} 8 \\ + 6 \\ \hline \end{array} \quad \begin{array}{r} 9 \\ - 3 \\ \hline \end{array} \quad \begin{array}{r} 7 \\ + 5 \\ \hline \end{array} \quad \begin{array}{r} 6 \\ + 3 \\ \hline \end{array} \quad \begin{array}{r} 5 \\ + 3 \\ \hline \end{array} \quad \begin{array}{r} 9 \\ - 6 \\ \hline \end{array}$$

$$\begin{array}{r} 9 \\ + 7 \\ \hline \end{array} \quad \begin{array}{r} 4 \\ + 2 \\ \hline \end{array} \quad \begin{array}{r} 3 \\ + 6 \\ \hline \end{array} \quad \begin{array}{r} 6 \\ + 8 \\ \hline \end{array} \quad \begin{array}{r} 5 \\ + 7 \\ \hline \end{array} \quad \begin{array}{r} 9 \\ - 3 \\ \hline \end{array} \quad \begin{array}{r} 6 \\ + 4 \\ \hline \end{array}$$

$$\begin{array}{r} 3 \\ + 6 \\ \hline \end{array} \quad \begin{array}{r} 8 \\ + 6 \\ \hline \end{array} \quad \begin{array}{r} 7 \\ + 9 \\ \hline \end{array} \quad \begin{array}{r} 4 \\ + 6 \\ \hline \end{array} \quad \begin{array}{r} 6 \\ + 3 \\ \hline \end{array} \quad \begin{array}{r} 3 \\ + 5 \\ \hline \end{array} \quad \begin{array}{r} 9 \\ - 6 \\ \hline \end{array}$$

Two Plus Two Is Not Five, Easy Methods To Learn Addition and Subtraction

Name _____

Practice **Number in the Middle** and **2 Ladder**.

7 + 5	4 + 2	8 − 2	3 + 5	6 + 2	6 − 2	7 + 9
6 + 8	6 + 4	10 − 2	9 + 7	8 + 6	2 + 8	7 + 5
7 + 9	2 + 6	2 + 4	6 − 2	6 + 8	6 + 4	8 + 2
10 − 2	7 + 5	4 − 2	8 + 6	5 + 7	5 + 3	4 − 2

Practice **Number in the Middle**, **Number Family 3•4•7**, and **Magic 9**.

4 + 6	9 + 4	7 − 3	3 + 4	7 + 5	6 + 9	3 + 5
8 + 6	4 + 3	9 + 2	9 + 8	7 − 4	6 + 8	3 + 4
7 − 4	4 + 6	2 + 4	6 + 8	9 + 9	3 + 4	5 + 7
3 + 9	7 + 5	9 + 7	5 + 3	8 + 6	7 − 3	3 + 5

Two Plus Two Is Not Five, Easy Methods To Learn Addition and Subtraction

Name _____

Practice **Number in the Middle** and **Double +1**.

8 + 6	5 + 7	4 + 5	3 + 5	4 + 3	2 + 3	4 + 6
5 + 4	6 + 8	3 + 4	9 + 7	7 + 5	8 + 6	3 + 4
7 + 9	4 + 5	3 + 2	5 + 7	6 + 4	5 + 3	6 + 8

Practice **Number in the Middle**, **Number Family 2•3•5**, and **Curvy Numbers**.

5 + 7	13 − 5	7 + 9	5 − 3	3 + 2	8 − 3	8 + 6
2 + 3	5 + 3	5 − 2	8 + 5	7 + 5	5 − 3	3 + 5
6 + 4	5 + 7	8 − 5	3 + 2	13 − 8	6 + 8	7 + 5
9 + 7	5 − 2	8 + 6	5 + 7	4 + 6	2 + 3	8 − 3
5 − 3	6 + 8	3 + 5	5 − 2	5 + 8	7 + 5	8 + 6

Two Plus Two Is Not Five, Easy Methods To Learn Addition and Subtraction

Name _____

TRICK Big Subtraction

Ask: What numbers are <u>bigger</u> or greater than **7**?

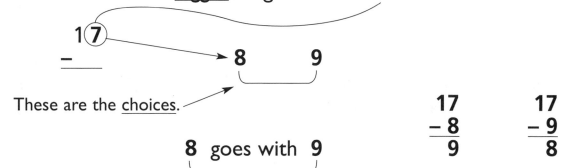

These are the <u>choices</u>.

8 goes with 9

17	17
− 8	− 9
9	8

• **9** is always the biggest choice!
• **9** always goes with the smallest choice.

Ask: What number is <u>bigger</u> or greater than **8**?

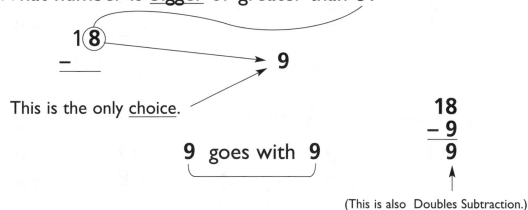

This is the only <u>choice</u>.

9 goes with 9

18
− 9
9

↑

(This is also <u>Doubles Subtraction</u>.)

Try **Big Subtraction**.

17	18	17	17	5	18	17
− 8	− 9	− 9	− 8	+ 5	− 9	− 9

2	17	18	10	17	17	18
+ 2	− 9	− 9	− 5	− 8	− 9	− 9

17	18	3	17	17	18	17
− 8	− 9	+ 3	− 8	− 9	− 9	− 8

Two Plus Two Is Not Five, Easy Methods To Learn Addition and Subtraction

Name _____

Practice **Big Subtraction** and **Backwards 1**.

17 − 8	18 − 9	7 − 1	17 − 8	18 − 9	9 − 1	17 − 8
5 − 1	17 − 9	17 − 8	8 − 1	17 − 8	17 − 9	3 − 1
10 − 1	17 − 8	6 − 1	17 − 9	18 − 9	4 − 1	18 − 9
17 − 9	2 − 1	18 − 9	17 − 8	9 − 1	17 − 8	10 − 1

Practice **Big Subtraction** and **2 Ladder**.

18 − 9	17 − 9	2 + 6	10 − 2	17 − 8	6 − 2	17 − 9
8 − 2	17 − 8	8 + 2	18 − 9	4 − 2	17 − 9	6 + 2
10 − 2	18 − 9	17 − 9	2 + 4	17 − 8	2 + 8	18 − 9
4 + 2	17 − 8	6 − 2	18 − 9	8 − 2	17 − 9	8 − 2

Name _____

More Big Subtraction

Ask: What numbers are <u>bigger</u> or greater than **6**?

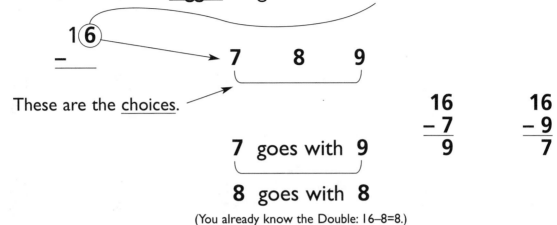

1**6**
– ___   → **7   8   9**

These are the <u>choices</u>. →

7 goes with **9**

8 goes with **8**

(You already know the <u>Double</u>: 16–8=8.)

$$\begin{array}{r} 16 \\ -\ 7 \\ \hline 9 \end{array} \qquad \begin{array}{r} 16 \\ -\ 9 \\ \hline 7 \end{array}$$

• **9** is always the biggest choice!
• **9** always goes with the smallest choice.

Try **Big Subtraction**.

$$\begin{array}{r} 16 \\ -\ 7 \\ \hline \end{array} \quad \begin{array}{r} 4 \\ +\ 4 \\ \hline \end{array} \quad \begin{array}{r} 16 \\ -\ 9 \\ \hline \end{array} \quad \begin{array}{r} 3 \\ +\ 3 \\ \hline \end{array} \quad \begin{array}{r} 17 \\ -\ 8 \\ \hline \end{array} \quad \begin{array}{r} 18 \\ -\ 9 \\ \hline \end{array} \quad \begin{array}{r} 17 \\ -\ 9 \\ \hline \end{array}$$

$$\begin{array}{r} 17 \\ -\ 8 \\ \hline \end{array} \quad \begin{array}{r} 16 \\ -\ 9 \\ \hline \end{array} \quad \begin{array}{r} 7 \\ +\ 7 \\ \hline \end{array} \quad \begin{array}{r} 16 \\ -\ 7 \\ \hline \end{array} \quad \begin{array}{r} 18 \\ -\ 9 \\ \hline \end{array} \quad \begin{array}{r} 17 \\ -\ 9 \\ \hline \end{array} \quad \begin{array}{r} 5 \\ +\ 5 \\ \hline \end{array}$$

$$\begin{array}{r} 16 \\ -\ 9 \\ \hline \end{array} \quad \begin{array}{r} 17 \\ -\ 8 \\ \hline \end{array} \quad \begin{array}{r} 18 \\ -\ 9 \\ \hline \end{array} \quad \begin{array}{r} 2 \\ +\ 2 \\ \hline \end{array} \quad \begin{array}{r} 17 \\ -\ 9 \\ \hline \end{array} \quad \begin{array}{r} 16 \\ -\ 7 \\ \hline \end{array} \quad \begin{array}{r} 17 \\ -\ 8 \\ \hline \end{array}$$

$$\begin{array}{r} 18 \\ -\ 9 \\ \hline \end{array} \quad \begin{array}{r} 16 \\ -\ 7 \\ \hline \end{array} \quad \begin{array}{r} 17 \\ -\ 9 \\ \hline \end{array} \quad \begin{array}{r} 16 \\ -\ 9 \\ \hline \end{array} \quad \begin{array}{r} 3 \\ +\ 3 \\ \hline \end{array} \quad \begin{array}{r} 17 \\ -\ 8 \\ \hline \end{array} \quad \begin{array}{r} 16 \\ -\ 9 \\ \hline \end{array}$$

Name _____

Practice **Big Subtraction** and **Right Next to Each Other**.

16 − 7	9 − 8	17 − 8	16 − 9	4 − 3	16 − 9	8 − 7
17 − 9	16 − 9	18 − 9	6 − 5	17 − 9	17 − 8	16 − 7
5 − 4	10 − 9	16 − 7	8 − 7	7 − 6	18 − 9	17 − 9
18 − 9	6 − 5	16 − 9	17 − 8	16 − 7	3 − 2	16 − 9

Practice **Big Subtraction**, **Curvy Numbers**, and **Count by 3s**.

16 − 9	8 − 3	17 − 8	3 + 6	16 − 7	13 − 5	9 − 6
17 − 9	16 − 7	6 + 3	8 + 5	16 − 9	9 − 3	8 − 5
5 + 3	17 − 8	9 − 6	13 − 8	18 − 9	16 − 7	3 + 6
9 − 3	5 + 8	16 − 9	17 − 9	6 + 3	3 + 5	18 − 9

Two Plus Two Is Not Five, Easy Methods To Learn Addition and Subtraction

Name _____

More Big Subtraction

Ask: What numbers are <u>bigger</u> or greater than **5**?

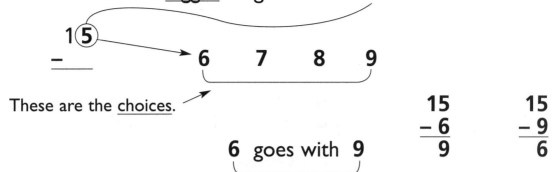

1**⑤**

− ___ → **6**   **7**   **8**   **9**

These are the <u>choices</u>.

6 goes with **9**

$$\begin{array}{r} 15 \\ -\ 6 \\ \hline 9 \end{array}$$ $$\begin{array}{r} 15 \\ -\ 9 \\ \hline 6 \end{array}$$

- **9** is always the biggest choice!
- **9** always goes with the smallest choice.

Try **Big Subtraction**.

$\begin{array}{r}15\\-\ 6\\\hline\end{array}$	$\begin{array}{r}15\\-\ 9\\\hline\end{array}$	$\begin{array}{r}17\\-\ 8\\\hline\end{array}$	$\begin{array}{r}4\\+\ 4\\\hline\end{array}$	$\begin{array}{r}15\\-\ 9\\\hline\end{array}$	$\begin{array}{r}16\\-\ 7\\\hline\end{array}$	$\begin{array}{r}18\\-\ 9\\\hline\end{array}$
$\begin{array}{r}17\\-\ 9\\\hline\end{array}$	$\begin{array}{r}16\\-\ 9\\\hline\end{array}$	$\begin{array}{r}15\\-\ 6\\\hline\end{array}$	$\begin{array}{r}17\\-\ 8\\\hline\end{array}$	$\begin{array}{r}1\\+\ 1\\\hline\end{array}$	$\begin{array}{r}15\\-\ 9\\\hline\end{array}$	$\begin{array}{r}2\\+\ 2\\\hline\end{array}$
$\begin{array}{r}15\\-\ 9\\\hline\end{array}$	$\begin{array}{r}16\\-\ 7\\\hline\end{array}$	$\begin{array}{r}6\\+\ 6\\\hline\end{array}$	$\begin{array}{r}16\\-\ 9\\\hline\end{array}$	$\begin{array}{r}15\\-\ 6\\\hline\end{array}$	$\begin{array}{r}17\\-\ 9\\\hline\end{array}$	$\begin{array}{r}16\\-\ 9\\\hline\end{array}$
$\begin{array}{r}16\\-\ 7\\\hline\end{array}$	$\begin{array}{r}15\\-\ 6\\\hline\end{array}$	$\begin{array}{r}18\\-\ 9\\\hline\end{array}$	$\begin{array}{r}15\\-\ 9\\\hline\end{array}$	$\begin{array}{r}7\\+\ 7\\\hline\end{array}$	$\begin{array}{r}16\\-\ 9\\\hline\end{array}$	$\begin{array}{r}15\\-\ 6\\\hline\end{array}$

Name _____

Practice **Big Subtraction** and **Double +1**.

15 − 9	4 + 3	4 + 5	16 − 9	18 − 9	2 + 3	5 + 4
17 − 8	16 − 7	5 + 4	3 + 4	15 − 6	4 + 3	16 − 9
3 + 2	17 − 9	18 − 9	5 + 4	2 + 3	15 − 9	4 + 5
16 − 7	15 − 6	3 + 4	17 − 8	3 + 2	17 − 9	15 − 9

Practice **Big Subtraction**.

17 − 9 = _____   15 − 6 = _____   16 − 9 = _____   17 − 8 = _____

16 − 7 = _____   18 − 9 = _____   17 − 8 = _____   15 − 9 = _____

17 − 8 = _____   15 − 9 = _____   16 − 9 = _____   17 − 9 = _____

16 − 7 = _____   18 − 9 = _____   15 − 6 = _____   17 − 8 = _____

17 − 9 = _____   15 − 6 = _____   16 − 9 = _____   15 − 9 = _____

16 − 7 = _____   18 − 9 = _____   15 − 9 = _____   15 − 6 = _____

Two Plus Two Is Not Five, Easy Methods To Learn Addition and Subtraction

Name _____

Practice **Big Subtraction** and **Doubles**.

15 − 6	6 + 6	8 + 8	15 − 9	16 − 9	16 − 7	8 − 4
17 − 9	16 − 8	15 − 6	17 − 8	3 + 3	15 − 9	14 − 7
16 − 9	15 − 6	9 + 9	16 − 8	10 − 5	17 − 8	15 − 6
5 + 5	16 − 7	15 − 9	16 − 7	17 − 9	15 − 9	12 − 6

Cumulative Practice.

16−9= _____   9+8= _____   15−9= _____   5−2= _____

8+5= _____   6−1= _____   7−6= _____   6+4= _____

17−9= _____   15−6= _____   8−2= _____   4−4= _____

9−6= _____   4+3= _____   16−9= _____   2+8= _____

10−5= _____   6+3= _____   15−6= _____   8+8= _____

4+5= _____   13−5= _____   7+7= _____   7−3= _____

15−9= _____   17−8= _____   4+9= _____   16−7= _____

Two Plus Two Is Not Five, Easy Methods To Learn Addition and Subtraction

Name _____

More <u>Big Subtraction</u>

Ask: What numbers are <u>bigger</u> or greater than **4**?

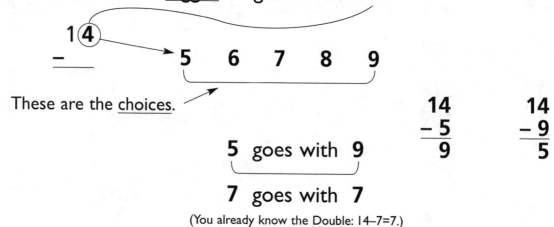

1④
−___   → **5   6   7   8   9**

These are the <u>choices</u>.

14	14
− 5	− 9
9	5

5 goes with **9**

7 goes with **7**

(You already know the <u>Double</u>: 14−7=7.)

• **9** is always the biggest choice!
• **9** always goes with the smallest choice.

Try **<u>Big Subtraction</u>**.

14	14	16	15	14	17	14
− 9	− 5	− 9	− 6	− 9	− 9	− 5

16	15	9	16	18	14	16
− 7	− 9	+ 9	− 9	− 9	− 9	− 7

17	15	17	14	7	15	14
− 8	− 6	− 9	− 9	+ 7	− 9	− 9

14	16	15	8	16	14	15
− 5	− 7	− 9	+ 8	− 9	− 5	− 6

Two Plus Two Is Not Five, Easy Methods To Learn Addition and Subtraction

Name _____

Practice **Big Subtraction** and **Zero**.

14 − 5	9 + 0	15 − 6	3 − 3	18 − 9	0 + 9	5 − 0
16 − 7	14 − 9	0 + 3	9 − 9	17 − 8	8 − 0	14 − 9
1 − 1	17 − 9	7 − 0	14 − 5	0 + 6	14 − 5	4 − 0
14 − 9	6 + 0	16 − 9	15 − 6	5 − 5	3 + 0	16 − 9

Practice **Big Subtraction**, **Number Families 2•3•5** and **3•4•7**.

15 − 9	17 − 8	14 − 5	7 − 3	2 + 3	18 − 9	4 + 3
7 − 4	5 − 3	15 − 6	17 − 9	14 − 9	16 − 9	7 − 4
17 − 9	5 − 2	16 − 7	15 − 9	17 − 8	14 − 5	3 + 2
3 + 4	14 − 9	15 − 9	7 − 4	5 − 3	15 − 6	14 − 9

Two Plus Two Is Not Five, Easy Methods To Learn Addition and Subtraction 117

Name _____

More Big Subtraction

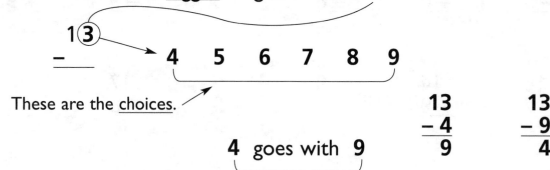

Ask: What numbers are <u>bigger</u> or greater than **3**?

These are the <u>choices</u>.

4 goes with **9**

13	13
− 4	− 9
9	4

- **9** is always the biggest choice!
- **9** always goes with the smallest choice.

Try **Big Subtraction**.

13	16	13	15	17	14	13
− 4	− 9	− 9	− 9	− 8	− 9	− 9

15	17	14	13	16	5	18
− 6	− 9	− 5	− 4	− 7	+ 5	− 9

13	6	15	14	18	14	13
− 9	+ 6	− 9	− 5	− 9	− 7	− 4

14	16	13	15	14	13	17
− 5	− 7	− 4	− 6	− 9	− 9	− 8

 Two Plus Two Is Not Five, Easy Methods To Learn Addition and Subtraction

Name _____

Practice **Big Subtraction** and **Curvy Numbers**.

13	5	13	16	13	14	8
− 9	+ 8	− 5	− 9	− 9	− 5	− 5

16	13	5	15	8	18	17
− 7	− 4	+ 8	− 9	− 3	− 9	− 9

8	13	17	15	8	13	5
− 5	− 8	− 8	− 6	+ 5	− 9	+ 3

13	8	8	13	14	13	13
− 4	+ 5	− 3	− 8	− 9	− 5	− 4

Practice **Big Subtraction**, **Number +1**, and **Double +1**.

13−4= _____   6+1= _____   4+3= _____   1+7= _____

16−9= _____   15−6= _____   1+8= _____   13−4= _____

14−5= _____   3+2= _____   13−9= _____   17−8= _____

4+1= _____   9+1= _____   16−7= _____   18−9= _____

17−9= _____   15−9= _____   4+5= _____   13−9= _____

3+4= _____   1+2= _____   13−9= _____   2+3= _____

3+1= _____   14−9= _____   5+4= _____   13−4= _____

Two Plus Two Is Not Five, Easy Methods To Learn Addition and Subtraction

Name _____

More Big Subtraction

Ask: What numbers are <u>bigger</u> or greater than **2**?

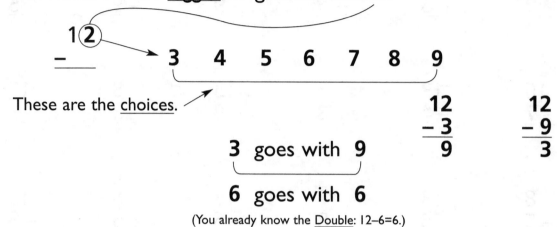

$1\textcircled{2}$

$-\underline{}$ → **3   4   5   6   7   8   9**

These are the <u>choices</u>. →

3 goes with **9**

6 goes with **6**

(You already know the <u>Double</u>: 12–6=6.)

$$\begin{array}{r} 12 \\ -\ 3 \\ \hline 9 \end{array} \qquad \begin{array}{r} 12 \\ -\ 9 \\ \hline 3 \end{array}$$

- **9** is always the biggest choice!
- **9** always goes with the smallest choice.

Try **Big Subtraction**.

12 − 9	15 − 6	12 − 3	14 − 5	13 − 9	12 − 9	16 − 7
17 − 9	12 − 3	13 − 4	18 − 9	4 + 4	17 − 8	12 − 9
14 − 9	16 − 9	12 − 9	15 − 9	13 − 4	12 − 3	14 − 9
12 − 3	3 + 3	13 − 9	12 − 3	12 − 9	16 − 7	13 − 9

Name _____

Practice **Big Subtraction** and **Doubles**.

12 − 3	4 + 4	16 − 8	13 − 9	14 − 7	3 + 3	12 − 9
16 − 7	2 + 2	5 + 5	6 − 3	12 − 9	12 − 6	15 − 9
6 + 6	10 − 5	14 − 9	8 − 4	7 + 7	12 − 3	14 − 5
17 − 8	12 − 3	8 + 8	12 − 9	13 − 4	18 − 9	4 − 2

Cumulative Practice.

3 + 6	12 − 9	3 − 3	4 − 2	13 − 8	15 − 6	4 + 5
12 − 3	4 − 1	14 − 9	1 + 5	16 − 9	8 − 2	7 − 6

13−4= _____   9+9= _____   7−4= _____   12−9= _____

9+4= _____   12−3= _____   6+2= _____   17−8= _____

14−5= _____   6+4= _____   13−9= _____   9−6= _____

Two Plus Two Is Not Five, Easy Methods To Learn Addition and Subtraction

Name _____

More <u>Big Subtraction</u>

Ask: What numbers are <u>bigger</u> or greater than **1**?

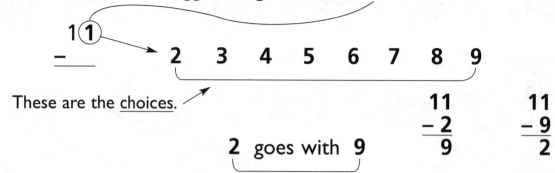

These are the <u>choices</u>.

2 goes with **9**

$$\begin{array}{r} 11 \\ -\ 2 \\ \hline 9 \end{array}$$

$$\begin{array}{r} 11 \\ -\ 9 \\ \hline 2 \end{array}$$

- **9** is always the biggest choice!
- **9** always goes with the smallest choice.

Try **<u>Big Subtraction</u>**.

$\begin{array}{r}11\\-\ 9\\\hline\end{array}$	$\begin{array}{r}11\\-\ 2\\\hline\end{array}$	$\begin{array}{r}15\\-\ 6\\\hline\end{array}$	$\begin{array}{r}13\\-\ 9\\\hline\end{array}$	$\begin{array}{r}11\\-\ 9\\\hline\end{array}$	$\begin{array}{r}14\\-\ 5\\\hline\end{array}$	$\begin{array}{r}17\\-\ 9\\\hline\end{array}$
$\begin{array}{r}12\\-\ 3\\\hline\end{array}$	$\begin{array}{r}16\\-\ 9\\\hline\end{array}$	$\begin{array}{r}11\\-\ 9\\\hline\end{array}$	$\begin{array}{r}15\\-\ 9\\\hline\end{array}$	$\begin{array}{r}16\\-\ 7\\\hline\end{array}$	$\begin{array}{r}11\\-\ 2\\\hline\end{array}$	$\begin{array}{r}14\\-\ 9\\\hline\end{array}$
$\begin{array}{r}17\\-\ 8\\\hline\end{array}$	$\begin{array}{r}11\\-\ 9\\\hline\end{array}$	$\begin{array}{r}13\\-\ 4\\\hline\end{array}$	$\begin{array}{r}11\\-\ 2\\\hline\end{array}$	$\begin{array}{r}12\\-\ 9\\\hline\end{array}$	$\begin{array}{r}13\\-\ 9\\\hline\end{array}$	$\begin{array}{r}12\\-\ 3\\\hline\end{array}$
$\begin{array}{r}13\\-\ 4\\\hline\end{array}$	$\begin{array}{r}12\\-\ 9\\\hline\end{array}$	$\begin{array}{r}11\\-\ 2\\\hline\end{array}$	$\begin{array}{r}18\\-\ 9\\\hline\end{array}$	$\begin{array}{r}14\\-\ 5\\\hline\end{array}$	$\begin{array}{r}12\\-\ 3\\\hline\end{array}$	$\begin{array}{r}11\\-\ 9\\\hline\end{array}$

Two Plus Two Is Not Five, Easy Methods To Learn Addition and Subtraction

Name _____

Practice **Big Subtraction** and **2 Ladder**.

11−9= _____   6+2= _____   12−9= _____   13−4= _____

10−2= _____   11−2= _____   8+2= _____   16−9= _____

8−2= _____   14−5= _____   15−9= _____   6−2= _____

11−9= _____   17−8= _____   2+6= _____   12−3= _____

14−9= _____   10−2= _____   13−9= _____   11−9= _____

4+2= _____   2+8= _____   11−2= _____   16−7= _____

11−2= _____   15−6= _____   8−2= _____   6+2= _____

Practice **Big Subtraction** and **Magic 9**.

11−2= _____   9+3= _____   17−8= _____   11−9= _____

14−5= _____   13−9= _____   9+9= _____   16−7= _____

6+9= _____   15−6= _____   11−9= _____   9+5= _____

11−9= _____   12−3= _____   9+4= _____   12−9= _____

5+9= _____   11−2= _____   13−4= _____   7+9= _____

17−9= _____   2+9= _____   9+8= _____   11−2= _____

Two Plus Two Is Not Five, Easy Methods To Learn Addition and Subtraction   **123**

Name _____

Cumulative Practice.

11 − 9	3 + 4	8 − 2	4 + 1	8 + 2	12 − 9	9 + 5
3 + 6	6 − 5	14 − 5	11 − 9	5 + 8	4 + 6	11 − 2
13 − 4	10 − 5	11 − 2	17 − 8	15 − 6	16 − 8	2 + 6
7 − 3	11 − 2	16 − 9	8 − 3	0 + 9	12 − 3	9 + 3

11−9= _____   15−9= _____   4+5= _____   13−8= _____

7+7= _____   6+4= _____   11−2= _____   9−8= _____

16−7= _____   5+3= _____   6−2= _____   14−9= _____

3+2= _____   11−2= _____   14−7= _____   1−1= _____

5+5= _____   12−9= _____   4+2= _____   11−9= _____

17−9= _____   13−9= _____   6+9= _____   12−3= _____

5−2= _____   9−0= _____   11−2= _____   9−3= _____

Name _____

Tiers 1, 2, 3, and 4 Review
Review **Straight Lines** and **Double +1**.

7 + 4	5 + 4	11 − 7	2 + 3	4 + 3	4 + 7	11 − 7
3 + 4	11 − 4	7 + 4	4 + 5	3 + 2	11 − 4	7 + 4
11 − 4	4 + 7	4 + 3	11 − 7	4 + 7	4 + 5	3 + 4
7 + 4	11 − 4	5 + 4	4 + 7	3 + 4	3 + 2	11 − 7

Review **Straight Lines** and **2 Ladder**.

4 + 7	2 + 8	11 − 4	4 + 7	2 + 4	11 − 7	8 − 2
11 − 4	6 − 2	7 + 4	8 + 2	4 + 7	10 − 2	11 − 4
2 + 6	4 + 7	4 − 2	7 + 4	8 − 2	7 + 4	6 + 2
11 − 4	4 + 7	4 + 2	6 − 2	10 − 2	11 − 7	7 + 4

Two Plus Two Is Not Five, Easy Methods To Learn Addition and Subtraction **125**

Name _____

Tiers 1, 2, 3, and 4 Review
Review __Straight Lines__ and __Big Subtraction__.

11	4	16	14	17	11	15
− 4	+ 7	− 7	− 5	− 9	− 7	− 9

12	11	7	18	11	11	16
− 9	− 4	+ 4	− 9	− 7	− 9	− 9

11	13	15	4	12	11	7
− 7	− 4	− 6	+ 7	− 3	− 4	+ 4

11	4	17	13	7	14	11
− 2	+ 7	− 8	− 9	+ 4	− 9	− 7

Review __Straight Lines__ and __Curvy Numbers__.

4	3	11	13	13	5	4
+ 7	+ 5	− 7	− 5	− 8	+ 8	+ 7

11	8	8	13	8	7	13
− 4	− 3	+ 5	− 8	− 5	+ 4	− 5

8	5	4	11	13	8	13
+ 5	+ 3	+ 7	− 4	− 5	− 5	− 8

7	8	13	3	11	13	5
+ 4	− 3	− 8	+ 5	− 7	− 5	+ 8

Name _____

Tiers 1, 2, 3, and 4 Review
Review **Number Family 4•5•9** and **Number in the Middle**.

$$
\begin{array}{cccccccc}
4 & 8 & 6 & 9 & 9 & 4 & 7 \\
+5 & +6 & +4 & -5 & -4 & +6 & +5 \\
\end{array}
$$

$$
\begin{array}{cccccccc}
9 & 9 & 6 & 3 & 7 & 9 & 5 \\
+7 & -5 & +8 & +5 & +9 & -4 & +4 \\
\end{array}
$$

$$
\begin{array}{cccccccc}
6 & 4 & 5 & 9 & 6 & 7 & 8 \\
+4 & +5 & +7 & -4 & +8 & +5 & +6 \\
\end{array}
$$

$$
\begin{array}{cccccccc}
5 & 2 & 9 & 8 & 5 & 9 & 5 \\
+3 & +4 & -5 & +6 & +4 & -4 & +7 \\
\end{array}
$$

Review **Number Family** and **Doubles**.

$$
\begin{array}{cccccccc}
5 & 9 & 6 & 9 & 14 & 5 & 4 \\
+4 & -4 & +6 & -5 & -7 & +5 & +5 \\
\end{array}
$$

$$
\begin{array}{cccccccc}
9 & 8 & 3 & 8 & 9 & 9 & 4 \\
-4 & +8 & +3 & -4 & -4 & +9 & -2 \\
\end{array}
$$

$$
\begin{array}{cccccccc}
12 & 4 & 9 & 4 & 18 & 10 & 9 \\
-6 & +3 & -5 & +5 & -9 & -5 & -5 \\
\end{array}
$$

$$
\begin{array}{cccccccc}
5 & 1 & 4 & 9 & 6 & 9 & 16 \\
+4 & +1 & +4 & -4 & -3 & -5 & -8 \\
\end{array}
$$

Two Plus Two Is Not Five, Easy Methods To Learn Addition and Subtraction   **127**

Name _____

Tiers 1, 2, 3, and 4 Review
Review **Number Family**, **Big Subtraction**, and **Zero**.

9 -5	13 -4	11 -9	4 $+5$	17 -8	12 -3	9 $+0$
4 $+0$	14 -5	5 $+4$	4 -4	9 -4	3 -0	13 -9
15 -9	0 $+2$	18 -9	9 -4	4 $+5$	11 -2	9 -5
5 -0	9 -5	16 -9	0 $+8$	9 -4	14 -9	1 -1

Review **Number Families** and **Straight Lines**.

9 -4	4 $+5$	11 -4	9 -5	3 $+4$	7 $+4$	7 -3
7 -4	4 $+7$	3 $+2$	11 -4	5 -3	9 -4	11 -7
4 $+5$	7 -3	7 $+4$	5 -2	4 $+3$	11 -4	9 -5
9 -5	11 -7	5 $+4$	4 $+7$	7 -4	2 $+3$	5 -3

Two Plus Two Is Not Five, Easy Methods To Learn Addition and Subtraction

Name _____

Tiers 1, 2, 3, and 4 Review
Review **Number in the Middle**, **2 Ladder**, and **Backwards 1**.

6 + 8	4 + 2	8 − 2	3 + 5	6 + 2	6 − 2	9 − 1
5 + 7	2 − 1	10 − 2	9 + 7	8 + 6	2 + 8	7 + 5
6 − 1	2 + 6	2 + 4	6 + 4	5 + 3	5 − 1	8 + 2
2 + 6	10 − 1	8 + 6	3 − 1	5 + 7	6 − 2	4 + 6

Review **Number in the Middle**, **Magic 9**, and **Right Next to Each Other**.

5+7= _____	9+5= _____	7−6= _____	4+9= _____
10−9= _____	4+6= _____	7+9= _____	8−7= _____
9+6= _____	6−5= _____	6+4= _____	9+3= _____
3−2= _____	7+5= _____	5+3= _____	9−8= _____
2+9= _____	4−3= _____	6+9= _____	6+8= _____
3+5= _____	9+7= _____	5+7= _____	5−4= _____
9+9= _____	8+6= _____	2+4= _____	8+9= _____

Two Plus Two Is Not Five, Easy Methods To Learn Addition and Subtraction   129

Name _____

Tiers 1, 2, 3, and 4 Review
Review **Number in the Middle**, **Number Family 4•5•9**, and **Count by 3s**.

$$\begin{array}{r} 7 \\ +\,5 \\ \hline \end{array} \qquad \begin{array}{r} 3 \\ +\,6 \\ \hline \end{array} \qquad \begin{array}{r} 9 \\ -\,5 \\ \hline \end{array} \qquad \begin{array}{r} 6 \\ +\,8 \\ \hline \end{array} \qquad \begin{array}{r} 9 \\ -\,3 \\ \hline \end{array} \qquad \begin{array}{r} 2 \\ +\,4 \\ \hline \end{array} \qquad \begin{array}{r} 5 \\ +\,4 \\ \hline \end{array}$$

$$\begin{array}{r} 6 \\ +\,3 \\ \hline \end{array} \qquad \begin{array}{r} 5 \\ +\,7 \\ \hline \end{array} \qquad \begin{array}{r} 8 \\ +\,6 \\ \hline \end{array} \qquad \begin{array}{r} 9 \\ -\,4 \\ \hline \end{array} \qquad \begin{array}{r} 4 \\ +\,5 \\ \hline \end{array} \qquad \begin{array}{r} 6 \\ +\,4 \\ \hline \end{array} \qquad \begin{array}{r} 9 \\ -\,6 \\ \hline \end{array}$$

$$\begin{array}{r} 9 \\ -\,3 \\ \hline \end{array} \qquad \begin{array}{r} 5 \\ +\,4 \\ \hline \end{array} \qquad \begin{array}{r} 3 \\ +\,6 \\ \hline \end{array} \qquad \begin{array}{r} 5 \\ +\,7 \\ \hline \end{array} \qquad \begin{array}{r} 9 \\ -\,6 \\ \hline \end{array} \qquad \begin{array}{r} 8 \\ +\,6 \\ \hline \end{array} \qquad \begin{array}{r} 9 \\ -\,4 \\ \hline \end{array}$$

$$\begin{array}{r} 6 \\ +\,8 \\ \hline \end{array} \qquad \begin{array}{r} 4 \\ +\,6 \\ \hline \end{array} \qquad \begin{array}{r} 7 \\ +\,9 \\ \hline \end{array} \qquad \begin{array}{r} 9 \\ -\,5 \\ \hline \end{array} \qquad \begin{array}{r} 5 \\ +\,3 \\ \hline \end{array} \qquad \begin{array}{r} 6 \\ +\,3 \\ \hline \end{array} \qquad \begin{array}{r} 7 \\ +\,5 \\ \hline \end{array}$$

Review **Number in the Middle**, **Straight Lines**, and **Curvy Numbers**.

6+8= _____   11−4= _____   7+5= _____   13−5= _____

4+6= _____   5+3= _____   5+8= _____   11−7= _____

13−8= _____   4+7= _____   8−3= _____   6+4= _____

7+5= _____   11−4= _____   3+5= _____   7+4= _____

8−5= _____   8+5= _____   4+7= _____   4+2= _____

6+8= _____   5+7= _____   13−5= _____   8+6= _____

11−7= _____   8−3= _____   7+5= _____   8−5= _____

Two Plus Two Is Not Five, Easy Methods To Learn Addition and Subtraction

Name _____

Tiers 1, 2, 3, and 4 Review
Review **Big Subtraction**, **Double +1**, and **Number Family 4•5•9**.

14 −9	4 +5	13 −9	11 −2	9 −5	17 −8	16 −7
4 +3	12 −9	2 +3	9 −5	18 −9	13 −4	3 +2
9 −4	3 +4	12 −3	15 −9	9 −4	17 −9	5 +4
16 −9	15 −6	14 −5	9 −5	11 −9	3 +4	9 −4

Review **Big Subtraction** and **Curvy Numbers**.

11 −9	8 +5	13 −4	3 +5	16 −7	12 −9	5 +8
17 −8	14 −9	15 −6	13 −5	8 −5	13 −8	11 −2
13 −5	12 −3	5 +8	15 −9	11 −2	14 −5	8 −3
16 −9	8 −3	13 −9	18 −9	13 −8	8 −5	17 −9

Two Plus Two Is Not Five, Easy Methods To Learn Addition and Subtraction

Name _____

Tiers 1, 2, 3, and 4 Review
Review **Big Subtraction** and **Number in the Middle**.

12 − 9	6 + 8	11 − 9	16 − 9	18 − 9	17 − 9	5 + 7
14 − 5	13 − 9	4 + 6	4 + 2	8 + 6	15 − 6	14 − 9
7 + 5	17 − 8	11 − 2	6 + 4	16 − 7	12 − 3	8 + 6
15 − 9	5 + 7	7 + 9	13 − 4	3 + 5	9 + 7	15 − 6

Review **Big Subtraction** and **Straight Lines**.

15−9= _____   13−4= _____   4+7= _____   11−4= _____

12−3= _____   11−7= _____   11−9= _____   17−9= _____

16−9= _____   14−5= _____   7+4= _____   13−9= _____

11−4= _____   18−9= _____   15−6= _____   4+7= _____

12−9= _____   16−7= _____   11−7= _____   14−9= _____

7+4= _____   11−2= _____   17−8= _____   11−4= _____

11−7= _____   12−3= _____   4+7= _____   12−9= _____

Two Plus Two Is Not Five, Easy Methods To Learn Addition and Subtraction

Name _____

Tiers 1, 2, 3, and 4 Review
Review all tricks.

10 − 2	9 + 8	2 + 3	3 + 6	11 − 4	17 − 8	7 + 7
0 + 7	4 + 6	8 + 5	14 − 9	13 − 5	5 + 3	1 + 8
6 + 6	15 − 9	8 + 2	10 − 1	9 − 4	5 + 9	4 + 7
8 − 3	16 − 8	4 + 5	3 − 3	10 − 5	7 − 3	9 − 6
13 − 4	2 + 2	7 + 5	4 − 2	9 − 5	14 − 7	7 − 4
6 − 2	11 − 7	7 + 1	4 − 3	8 − 5	16 − 7	5 + 7
4 + 3	12 − 9	2 + 6	6 + 8	11 − 2	3 − 0	6 + 9
9 + 7	13 − 8	4 − 1	5 − 4	9 − 3	5 + 8	7 + 4

Two Plus Two Is Not Five, Easy Methods To Learn Addition and Subtraction 133

Name _____

Tiers 1, 2, 3, and 4 Review
Review all tricks.

8 − 2	3 + 2	6 + 3	11 − 9	5 − 2	5 + 4	12 − 6
6 + 4	17 − 9	9 + 9	11 − 4	9 + 5	3 + 3	6 − 5
9 − 5	6 + 2	5 + 8	8 + 8	2 + 4	16 − 9	3 + 5
5 − 0	4 + 7	14 − 5	10 − 2	13 − 8	7 − 4	5 + 7

11−7= _____   7−1= _____   5+5= _____   18−9= _____

9+0= _____   12−3= _____   9+2= _____   8+5= _____

10−5= _____   8+6= _____   4+4= _____   5−3= _____

14−7= _____   13−9= _____   4−4= _____   7−6= _____

9−4= _____   2+8= _____   7+5= _____   8−3= _____

3+4= _____   8−5= _____   3+9= _____   7+4= _____

11−2= _____   6+8= _____   6−3= _____   15−6= _____

Tier 5

Instructions and Information

Start with any trick. The tricks may be introduced in any order except:

- The three **Double +1** sets of facts should be taught in the given sequence, but each set does not immediately have to follow the set before it.

- The **Family Pairs** should be taught before the related **Family Partners**, but the subtraction facts do not immediately have to follow the addition facts.

- The addition facts for **Lots of 4s** and **Stretch** should be presented before the respective subtraction facts, but the subtraction facts do not immediately have to follow the addition facts.

Page	Trick	Math fact cards to be assigned:
135-138	**2 Ladder**	10-8, 8-6, 6-4
139-140	**Double +1**	5+6, 6+5
141-142	**Double +1**	6+7, 7+6
143-146	**Double +1**	7+8, 8+7
147-148	**Family Pair**	2+7, 7+2
149-152	**Family Partners**	9-2, 9-7
153-154	**Lots of 4s**	4+8, 8+4
155-158	**Lots of 4s Subtraction**	12-4, 12-8
159-160	**Family Pair**	2+5, 5+2
161-164	**Family Partners**	7-2, 7-5
165-166	**Stretch**	3+7, 7+3
167-170	**Stretch Subtraction**	10-3, 10-7
171–186	**Review Pages**	

Tier 5 Answers

Page 135
2,8,6,8,4,2,2
10,2,2,6,2,4,8
2,4,6,2,10,8,6
4,8,2,6,2,2,8
8,4,2,8,10,6,2

Page 136
2,16,8,8,13,11,2
10,17,14,2,15,2,18
12,8,6,14,2,17,8
13,4,10,16,2,15,6
10,9,2,2,3,8,2
6,6,8,6,8,4,10
2,3,9,2,9,2,2
8,6,2,9,8,6,2

Page 137
8,4,10,12,2,2,14
6,2,8,10,8,8,12
6,2,10,10,14,12,2
14,2,8,2,8,2,10
2,10,2,4,9,8,3
8,9,9,4,6,9,2
6,8,7,6,10,4,8
2,2,10,9,2,9,2

Page 138
6,8,8,5,13,8,2
10,5,8,2,5,2,4
8,2,13,2,8,6,3
2,13,2,8,3,5,13
10,2,4,2
3,5,7,4
2,8,9,2
9,5,2,8
4,4,6,6
7,3,3,2
5,10,8,5

Page 139
11,10,11,10,11
11,5,11,5,11,12,11
5,11,0,11,7,3,11
9,7,14,11,3,11,1
11,4,10,9,11,5,11
7,11,0,11,9,11,7

Page 140
11,11,4,11,9,5,7
9,4,11,11,11,4,7
11,11,5,7,11,7,11
7,7,11,11,11,9,4
11,14,7,11
9,5,12,18
16,17,11,9
7,11,15,11
13,9,11,12
5,16,7,11
14,11,15,17

Page 141
13,12,13,12,13
13,12,9,13,4,7,13
5,13,11,9,8,13,14
9,8,1,8,9,7,7
13,10,11,10,6,13,1
5,7,8,13,8,11,8

Page 142
13,8,7,9,13,5,5
8,11,3,13,10,11,7
13,9,5,2,11,6,13
5,7,13,7,1,9,11
7,4,13,5,9,9,13
11,13,3,9,9,5,7
9,7,9,6,9,9,11
9,2,13,11,9,5,8

Page 143
15,14,15,14,15
15,6,15,14,13,11,15
5,15,18,6,7,15,7
13,3,15,10,11,4,15
17,13,9,15,9,8,5
15,8,11,16,2,15,13

Page 144
13,1,5,1,15,7,15
1,0,15,11,1,9,8
7,1,9,3,1,11,13
1,15,1,5,13,5,0
15,13,9,4,7,5,15
4,11,5,9,4,13,5
7,15,11,5,15,17,11
13,4,15,13,5,5,15

Page 145
9,11,6,13,7,9,4
15,9,11,15,9,3,11
4,7,15,6,11,15,3
5,13,11,9,15,11,7
15,12,8,5,14,15,8
5,11,15,13,10,5,13
14,3,13,12,15,5,9
10,7,13,8,8,15,11

Page 146
11,15,8,13,5,9,1
8,3,7,4,13,1,15
14,9,15,9,9,13,6
11,3,3,13,17,3,9
8,15,4,8
6,0,7,13
13,5,13,6
11,11,5,15
8,4,13,11
10,5,4,5
12,2,10,14

Page 147
9,4,9,9,14,9,18
9,14,9,9,18,9,9
18,9,4,9,9,14,9
9,6,9,16,9,6,2
9,9,12,9,3,9,9
10,7,9,8,9,8,9
4,4,5,9,18,9,14

Page 148
9,14,9,8,10,9,6
12,9,9,14,9,12,9
9,10,6,9,8,9,12
9,9,9,2,9,4,9
7,9,4,9,9,9,9
8,9,9,9,3,9,6
9,9,9,4,9,8,9
3,9,9,5,9,2,9

Page 149
7
9,7,7,9,2,2,7
9,2,2,2,9,7,2
2,16,7,17,9,2,11
12,9,15,2,7,14,9
13,7,18,14,2,9,7

Page 150
9,7,3,2,9,0,7
2,6,7,9,2,7,9
9,9,9,8,7,2,0
7,4,2,6,9,9,7
2,9,8,9,3,9,1
9,6,9,7,9,2,9
9,3,2,9,6,9,7
9,2,9,6,9,7,3

Page 151
9,7,9,4,7,5,9
2,5,9,7,2,4,2
4,9,7,9,7,2,5
9,7,9,2,4,9,9
2,11,9,7,9,4,11
7,7,4,9,2,7,9
11,4,2,7,9,11,2
9,11,7,4,11,9,7

Page 152
7,13,9,8,9,8,5
5,8,2,9,5,7,3
13,2,8,13,5,3,9
14,5,9,9,16,10,13
3,10,9,3,7,7,5
8,2,12,15
5,4,7,9
1,4,3,12
9,0,11,9
9,14,9,5

Page 153
12,8,12,4,12,8,12
8,12,16,12,8,12,12
12,10,12,12,12,7,12
5,12,9,8,12,12,7
12,16,0,14,12,5,12
12,8,12,12,7,12,8

Page 154
12,1,12,1,1,12,1
1,12,1,12,12,1,12
12,1,1,12,1,12,1
12,16,6,12,4,6,12
2,12,12,14,9,12,12
12,5,8,12,3,12,16
8,12,2,7,12,10,12
12,18,4,12,8,12,12

Page 155
12,8,12,8,8,4,12
4,4,12,4,12,8,4
12,4,6,9,4,9,12
8,3,4,9,6,12,8
6,9,8,4,12,3,12
4,12,3,9,8,4,9

Page 156
4,13,5,12,12,5,8
13,5,8,3,4,13,8
12,13,8,4,12,8,5
8,3,12,5,4,12,8
8,12,12,14,4,10,14
8,4,12,12,10,8,12
12,14,8,8,4,12,14
4,6,10,12,16,12,12

Page 157
12,4,12,8,11,4,12
11,4,8,12,8,11,7
4,7,11,4,12,4,4
7,8,4,11,7,12,11
12,2,4,7,9,8,4
9,12,8,12,5,9,9
4,9,12,9,9,12,8
9,8,4,6,4,3,12

Page 158
9,6,12,5,7,11,12
4,16,5,17,4,12,9
4,9,12,13,10,14,12
7,14,0,8,1,7,3
12,7,8,2,11,8,9
7,12,8,8
4,4,9,12
13,8,4,3
7,5,6,6
8,8,6,12
10,4,5,11

Page 159
5,2 or 2,5
7,10,7,7,4,7,8
7,14,7,7,5,7,7
4,7,7,3,7,10,7
7,9,7,7,7,3,9
2,7,9,7,9,7,7
10,5,7,9,7,9,7
4,4,9,7,6,7,8

Page 160
7,11,7,4,7,7,11
11,7,7,11,7,4,7
7,7,11,7,11,7,7
7,7,14,3,7,12,7
9,7,17,7,13,7,7
16,8,10,7,4,7,11
7,15,7,5,7,13,3
10,7,16,7,17,6,7

Page 161
5
7,5,7,5,7,2,2
5,2,9,2,5,1,1
5,6,2,1,9,3,7
2,1,1,6,5,7,9

Page 162
5,8,2,13,7,9,7
5,7,5,2,5,4,7
2,13,5,3,2,7,6
8,7,5,5,13,7,7
2,18,5,7,7,4,5
7,16,5,6,2,7,14
8,7,4,2,10,5,7
12,5,7,9,2,7,3

Page 163
7,10,14,5,8,12,2
5,12,2,7,14,8,7
6,16,7,12,7,5,10
2,6,5,14,12,7,8
5,7,5,1,9,0,4
9,6,5,4,7,3,2
2,5,9,2,0,7,8
7,4,7,5,5,4,9

Page 164
2,8,5,10,7,4,7
13,5,5,10,6,13,0
7,11,8,6,2,12,4
10,4,7,14,1,3,9
9,4,9,4,11,5,16
3,8,9,7
13,5,16,5
7,2,1,12
7,3,5,8
2,3,14,6
13,9,7,16

Page 165
10,10,7,10,3,10
10,6,10,6,10,8,10
9,10,7,10,3,10,2
10,10,7,5,10,3,10
4,9,10,5,8,10,4

Page 166
10,6,10,1,8,10,10
1,12,7,18,10,1,10
9,10,1,1,14,10,1
1,10,3,10,1,4,16
10,11,4,10
7,13,5,10
5,7,10,3
10,10,13,11
8,11,10,8
13,3,11,10
4,10,8,8

Page 167
10,3,3,7,7,10,3
7,7,10,3,7,3,10
3,10,4,7,9,5,10
9,5,7,9,10,4,3
10,4,9,7,10,3,5
3,5,10,4,10,9,7

Page 168
7,14,3,3,16,10,0
3,7,17,7,13,18,10
3,0,10,15,0,3,11
10,7,12,7,3,3,7
10,5,7,2,7,7,3
3,3,4,3,7,10,3
5,10,7,2,3,4,2
3,4,5,3,7,10,7

Page 169
10,7,9,6,10,9,9
3,3,9,10,4,10,7
5,10,7,7,3,8,9
3,2,10,9,10,7,3
10,14,9,6
10,3,3,8
12,9,7,3
14,10,10,3
9,7,10,14
3,12,10,7
10,6,14,12

Page 170
7,2,9,9,7,10,9
3,0,3,10,9,7,10
9,16,6,13,10,10,7
3,7,3,1,7,8,12
14,4,7,9,11,8,4
10,4,9,5,9,3,18
4,16,8,10,6,9,7
13,3,11,14,5,3,12

Page 171
2,14,2,12,2,2,12
2,2,14,2,2,2,2
2,10,8,2,2,14,2
2,12,2,8,2,2,10
2,7,2,11
2,2,11,4
2,11,2,11
4,2,11,2
2,2,4,2
2,7,2,2
2,11,2,2

Page 172
2,8,2,5,2,1,2
13,2,1,3,1,2,2
1,5,8,2,1,13,1
8,2,1,2,1,2,2
2,9,2,3,8,5,10
9,2,3,2,6,9,2
7,2,8,6,9,9,9
2,2,4,9,2,4,9

Page 173
6,12,10,10,2,8,2
16,6,2,14,5,6,2
7,8,4,8,8,4,6
2,3,10,2,8,4,2
10,2,3,10,2,7,8
10,8,8,6,7,6,3
2,10,7,2,3,10,2
10,3,6,10,4,7,10

Page 174
6,2,4,8,12,8,8
10,6,8,12,2,4,2
4,12,2,4,8,8,10
12,8,12,2,2,12,6
2,8,9,9
9,4,10,5
6,4,6,2
2,9,6,8
9,7,2,3
6,10,4,8
9,2,9,8

Page 175
13,9,3,10,15,7,11
10,11,15,17,3,5,10
7,13,7,11,10,15,9
3,11,7,10,15,7,7
15,15,9,13
13,17,13,7
12,16,5,11
15,11,14,18
11,12,5,13
11,7,14,13
16,15,9,17

Page 176
13,9,1,2,2,15,6
9,2,2,11,5,2,9
2,2,4,7,2,8,2
2,15,2,2,7,13,11
11,13,8,8
2,7,9,15
10,4,13,2
7,15,6,8
2,5,2,6
11,2,10,9
15,2,13,5

Page 177
9,12,2,12,9,8,7
12,4,9,7,8,12,9
9,7,12,2,4,2,8
2,9,2,2,9,2,2
2,7,2,9,2,2,2
7,2,2,9,2,9,7
2,2,9,2,7,2,2
9,2,7,2,2,2,9

Page 178
2,10,9,2,9,7,2
8,8,2,9,2,6,7
2,2,9,4,10,9,8
2,7,2,7,6,2,9
9,2,13,9
15,7,7,9
2,11,15,5
9,7,9,9
13,11,2,7
7,15,9,13
17,9,15,5

Page 179
12,4,7,12,2,6,11
4,8,8,8,11,12,4
12,7,4,11,4,2,12
11,2,4,4,11,10,8
6,8,8,10,7,11,12
12,8,13,11,4,7,12
5,12,4,15,9,8,15
12,9,8,12,4,12,13

Page 180
4,2,5,12,2,2,0
5,12,2,8,1,2,12
2,6,12,0,2,4,2
2,8,2,2,12,2,8
8,12,10,6,9,7,2
10,3,4,8,12,8,10
9,12,3,4,10,7,9
12,4,8,10,3,12,7

Page 181
5,7,13,2,7,15,11
15,13,7,5,2,7,7
7,15,5,13,7,9,5
13,9,2,17,15,11,7
7,10,2,6
2,8,3,8
9,7,6,5
6,2,6,7
7,5,9,2
10,3,4,2
5,9,7,9

Page 182
5,4,4,8,12,2,7
2,9,12,7,5,12,8
7,4,2,5,7,12,2
8,7,5,4,3,7,12
9,7,7,2,4,5,9
9,7,9,6,2,9,7
5,9,7,7,3,2,2
9,8,7,9,9,9,7

Page 183
10,4,10,7,10,11,7
7,11,3,11,7,4,10
11,10,7,4,11,10,3
11,3,10,3,7,4,11
3,2,9,2,2,7,7
5,10,7,7,2,9,10
2,2,7,10,5,2,2
9,10,7,7,3,2,2

Page 184
3,13,10,7,5,3,13
10,3,8,10,7,13,3
13,10,8,5,10,8,8
7,8,3,3,5,5,10
10,4,12,7
3,10,7,12
12,12,8,10
8,7,10,4
12,10,12,3
4,3,10,8
7,12,3,12

Page 185
9,13,9,7,7,9,7
4,15,2,10,3,5,10
2,11,2,8,13,5,12
2,5,9,1,7,5,8
11,12,9,4,9,5,14
7,15,5,3,8,10,11
3,4,12,15,4,10,2
2,3,6,13,4,5,13

Page 186
7,1,14,14,8,4,6
10,3,4,12,8,11,10
7,8,16,2,12,17,7
9,9,11,8,15,7,13
9,16,5,9,5,10,13
4,2,4,12,8,2,2
5,14,0,3,10,7,2
7,2,6,11,10,15,9

Name _____

TRICK 2 Ladder Subtraction

Count backwards by 2. Go down a 2-step.

These are also **Looks Like** <u>Number in the Middle</u>.

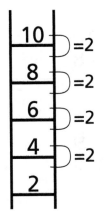

So the answer = **2**

$$\begin{array}{r} 10 \\ -\ 8 \\ \hline 2 \end{array} \qquad \begin{array}{r} 8 \\ -\ 6 \\ \hline 2 \end{array} \qquad \begin{array}{r} 6 \\ -\ 4 \\ \hline 2 \end{array} \qquad \begin{array}{r} 4 \\ -\ 2 \\ \hline 2 \end{array}$$

(This is also <u>Doubles</u>.)

Practice **2 Ladder**. Mark — **Looks Like Number in the Middle**.

$\begin{array}{r}8\\-6\end{array}$	$\begin{array}{r}10\\-2\end{array}$	$\begin{array}{r}8\\-2\end{array}$	$\begin{array}{r}6\\+2\end{array}$	$\begin{array}{r}6\\-2\end{array}$	$\begin{array}{r}10\\-8\end{array}$	$\begin{array}{r}6\\-4\end{array}$
$\begin{array}{r}8\\+2\end{array}$	$\begin{array}{r}10\\-8\end{array}$	$\begin{array}{r}8\\-6\end{array}$	$\begin{array}{r}8\\-2\end{array}$	$\begin{array}{r}6\\-4\end{array}$	$\begin{array}{r}6\\-2\end{array}$	$\begin{array}{r}10\\-2\end{array}$
$\begin{array}{r}4\\-2\end{array}$	$\begin{array}{r}2\\+2\end{array}$	$\begin{array}{r}2\\+4\end{array}$	$\begin{array}{r}8\\-6\end{array}$	$\begin{array}{r}2\\+8\end{array}$	$\begin{array}{r}10\\-2\end{array}$	$\begin{array}{r}8\\-2\end{array}$
$\begin{array}{r}6\\-2\end{array}$	$\begin{array}{r}2\\+6\end{array}$	$\begin{array}{r}6\\-4\end{array}$	$\begin{array}{r}8\\-2\end{array}$	$\begin{array}{r}10\\-8\end{array}$	$\begin{array}{r}8\\-6\end{array}$	$\begin{array}{r}6\\+2\end{array}$
$\begin{array}{r}10\\-2\end{array}$	$\begin{array}{r}6\\-2\end{array}$	$\begin{array}{r}10\\-8\end{array}$	$\begin{array}{r}2\\+6\end{array}$	$\begin{array}{r}8\\+2\end{array}$	$\begin{array}{r}4\\+2\end{array}$	$\begin{array}{r}6\\-4\end{array}$

Two Plus Two Is Not Five, Easy Methods To Learn Addition and Subtraction   **135**

Name _____

Practice **2 Ladder** and **Magic 9**.

10 − 8	9 + 7	10 − 2	6 + 2	9 + 4	2 + 9	6 − 4
8 + 2	8 + 9	5 + 9	8 − 6	6 + 9	10 − 8	9 + 9
3 + 9	2 + 6	4 + 2	9 + 5	6 − 4	9 + 8	10 − 2
4 + 9	6 − 2	2 + 8	7 + 9	8 − 6	9 + 6	8 − 2

Practice **2 Ladder** and **Count by 3s**.

8 + 2	6 + 3	10 − 8	6 − 4	9 − 6	6 + 2	8 − 6
2 + 4	8 − 2	2 + 6	9 − 3	10 − 2	6 − 2	2 + 8
8 − 6	9 − 6	3 + 6	10 − 8	3 + 6	4 − 2	6 − 4
10 − 2	4 + 2	8 − 6	6 + 3	2 + 6	9 − 3	10 − 8

Name _____

Practice **2 Ladder** and **Number in the Middle**.

2 + 6	6 − 2	2 + 8	5 + 7	8 − 6	6 − 4	8 + 6
8 − 2	10 − 8	3 + 5	4 + 6	10 − 2	6 + 2	7 + 5
4 + 2	8 − 6	6 + 4	8 + 2	6 + 8	5 + 7	8 − 6
6 + 8	6 − 4	5 + 3	4 − 2	3 + 5	10 − 8	6 + 4

Practice **2 Ladder** and **Big Subtraction**.

6 − 4	2 + 8	8 − 6	13 − 9	14 − 5	10 − 2	12 − 9
2 + 6	17 − 8	13 − 4	6 − 2	8 − 2	11 − 2	10 − 8
15 − 9	10 − 2	16 − 9	4 + 2	2 + 8	6 − 2	17 − 9
10 − 8	6 − 4	8 + 2	12 − 3	8 − 6	16 − 7	6 − 4

Two Plus Two Is Not Five, Easy Methods To Learn Addition and Subtraction **137**

Name _____

Practice **2 Ladder** and **Curvy Numbers**.

2 + 4	6 + 2	10 − 2	8 − 3	8 + 5	13 − 5	8 − 6

2 + 8	13 − 8	5 + 3	6 − 4	8 − 3	10 − 8	6 − 2

13 − 5	8 − 6	5 + 8	4 − 2	2 + 6	8 − 2	8 − 5

10 − 8	5 + 8	6 − 4	10 − 2	8 − 5	13 − 8	5 + 8

Practice **2 Ladder** and **Number Families 2•3•5**, **4•5•9**, and **3•4•7**.

2+8= _____	8−6= _____	9−5= _____	10−8= _____
7−4= _____	2+3= _____	3+4= _____	7−3= _____
10−8= _____	6+2= _____	4+5= _____	6−4= _____
5+4= _____	9−4= _____	5−3= _____	2+6= _____
7−3= _____	6−2= _____	4+2= _____	8−2= _____
4+3= _____	7−4= _____	5−2= _____	10−8= _____
9−4= _____	8+2= _____	10−2= _____	2+3= _____

Name _____

TRICK Double +1   Looks like <u>Right Next to Each Other.</u>

Double the lesser number and add 1.

⑤
+ 6
―――
11

5 ☐☐☐☐☐
+ 5 ☐☐☐☐☐ + 1 more ▨ =
―――
10
+ 1

5 ☐☐☐☐☐
+ 6 ☐☐☐☐☐▨
―――
11

LOOK. These are the same.

| ⑤
+ 6
11 | 6
+⑤
11 | 6
+ 5 | 5
+ 5 | 6
+ 5 | 5
+ 5 | 5
+ 6 |

Practice. Mark) **Double +1**.

| 6)
+ 5 | 3)
+ 2 | 5
+ 6 | 1
+ 4 | 6
+ 5 | 6
+ 6 | 5
+ 6 |

| 2
+ 3 | 5
+ 6 | 5
− 5 | 5
+ 6 | 4
+ 3 | 6
− 3 | 6
+ 5 |

| 5
+ 4 | 3
+ 4 | 7
+ 7 | 6
+ 5 | 4
− 1 | 5
+ 6 | 7
− 6 |

| 6
+ 5 | 2
+ 2 | 5
+ 5 | 4
+ 5 | 5
+ 6 | 2
+ 3 | 5
+ 6 |

| 3
+ 4 | 6
+ 5 | 8
− 8 | 5
+ 6 | 9
− 0 | 6
+ 5 | 4
+ 3 |

Name _____

Practice **Double +1** and **Straight Lines**.

6 + 5	7 + 4	11 − 7	5 + 6	4 + 5	3 + 2	11 − 4

5 + 4	11 − 7	5 + 6	4 + 7	6 + 5	11 − 7	4 + 3

7 + 4	5 + 6	2 + 3	11 − 4	4 + 7	3 + 4	6 + 5

11 − 4	3 + 4	4 + 7	5 + 6	7 + 4	5 + 4	11 − 7

Practice **Double +1** and **Magic 9**.

5+6= _____	5+9= _____	3+4= _____	6+5= _____
5+4= _____	3+2= _____	3+9= _____	9+9= _____
7+9= _____	9+8= _____	5+6= _____	4+5= _____
4+3= _____	9+2= _____	9+6= _____	6+5= _____
4+9= _____	5+4= _____	6+5= _____	9+3= _____
2+3= _____	9+7= _____	4+3= _____	2+9= _____
9+5= _____	5+6= _____	6+9= _____	8+9= _____

Name _____

More Double +1.   Looks like Right Next to Each Other.

Double the lesser number and add 1.

⑥
+ 7

13

6 ☐☐☐☐☐☐
+ 6 ☐☐☐☐☐☐ + 1 more ▨ =

12
+ 1

6 ☐☐☐☐☐☐
+ 7 ☐☐☐☐☐☐▨

13

LOOK. These are the same.

⑥	7
+ 7	+⑥
13	**13**

6
+ 7

6
+ 6

6
+ 7

6
+ 6

7
+ 6

Practice. Mark) **Double +1**.

6)
+ 7

6
+ 6

4
+ 5

7
+ 6

3
+ 1

8
− 1

6
+ 7

3
+ 2

6
+ 7

5
+ 6

1
+ 8

10
− 2

7
+ 6

7
+ 7

5
+ 4

16
− 8

8
− 7

4
+ 4

5
+ 4

3
+ 4

14
− 7

7
+ 6

5
+ 5

5
+ 6

8
+ 2

12
− 6

6
+ 7

5
− 4

2
+ 3

4
+ 3

1
+ 7

7
+ 6

2
+ 6

6
+ 5

8
− 0

Name _____

Practice **Double +1**, **Backwards 1**, and **Number +1**.

7	1	8	5	6	6	2
+ 6	+ 7	− 1	+ 4	+ 7	− 1	+ 3

9	5	2	7	1	6	3
− 1	+ 6	+ 1	+ 6	+ 9	+ 5	+ 4

6	10	1	3	5	5	6
+ 7	− 1	+ 4	− 1	+ 6	+ 1	+ 7

3	6	7	4	2	4	6
+ 2	+ 1	+ 6	+ 3	− 1	+ 5	+ 5

Practice **Double +1** and **Big Subtraction**.

3	13	6	14	15	11	6
+ 4	− 9	+ 7	− 9	− 6	− 2	+ 7

5	7	12	5	17	3	16
+ 6	+ 6	− 9	+ 4	− 8	+ 2	− 9

14	3	13	15	4	12	6
− 5	+ 4	− 4	− 9	+ 5	− 3	+ 5

5	11	6	5	16	3	17
+ 4	− 9	+ 7	+ 6	− 7	+ 2	− 9

Name _____

More Double +1.   Looks like Right Next to Each Other.

Double the lesser number and add 1.

$$
\begin{array}{r} ⑦ \\ +\ 8 \\ \hline 15 \end{array}
\qquad
\begin{array}{r} 7 \\ +\ 7 \\ \hline 14 \end{array}
\begin{array}{c} \square\square\square\square\square\square\square \\ \square\square\square\square\square\square\square \end{array} + 1\ \text{more}\ \blacksquare =
\begin{array}{r} 7 \\ +\ 8 \\ \hline \mathbf{15} \end{array}
\begin{array}{c} \square\square\square\square\square\square\square \\ \square\square\square\square\square\square\square\blacksquare \end{array}
$$

$$+\ 1$$

LOOK. These are the same.

$$
\begin{array}{r} ⑦ \\ +\ 8 \\ \hline 15 \end{array}
\qquad
\begin{array}{r} 8 \\ +⑦ \\ \hline 15 \end{array}
\qquad
\begin{array}{r} 8 \\ +\ 7 \\ \hline \end{array}
\qquad
\begin{array}{r} 7 \\ +\ 7 \\ \hline \end{array}
\qquad
\begin{array}{r} 8 \\ +\ 7 \\ \hline \end{array}
\qquad
\begin{array}{r} 7 \\ +\ 7 \\ \hline \end{array}
\qquad
\begin{array}{r} 7 \\ +\ 8 \\ \hline \end{array}
$$

(You already know Magic 9: 8+9 and 9+8.)

Practice **Double +1** and **Doubles**.   Mark ⟩ **Double +1**.

$$
\begin{array}{r} 7 \\ +\ 8\ ⟩ \\ \hline \end{array}
\qquad
\begin{array}{r} 3 \\ +\ 3 \\ \hline \end{array}
\qquad
\begin{array}{r} 8 \\ +\ 7 \\ \hline \end{array}
\qquad
\begin{array}{r} 7 \\ +\ 7 \\ \hline \end{array}
\qquad
\begin{array}{r} 6 \\ +\ 7 \\ \hline \end{array}
\qquad
\begin{array}{r} 5 \\ +\ 6 \\ \hline \end{array}
\qquad
\begin{array}{r} 7 \\ +\ 8 \\ \hline \end{array}
$$

$$
\begin{array}{r} 10 \\ -\ 5 \\ \hline \end{array}
\qquad
\begin{array}{r} 8 \\ +\ 7 \\ \hline \end{array}
\qquad
\begin{array}{r} 9 \\ +\ 9 \\ \hline \end{array}
\qquad
\begin{array}{r} 12 \\ -\ 6 \\ \hline \end{array}
\qquad
\begin{array}{r} 14 \\ -\ 7 \\ \hline \end{array}
\qquad
\begin{array}{r} 8 \\ +\ 7 \\ \hline \end{array}
\qquad
\begin{array}{r} 4 \\ +\ 3 \\ \hline \end{array}
$$

$$
\begin{array}{r} 7 \\ +\ 6 \\ \hline \end{array}
\qquad
\begin{array}{r} 6 \\ -\ 3 \\ \hline \end{array}
\qquad
\begin{array}{r} 7 \\ +\ 8 \\ \hline \end{array}
\qquad
\begin{array}{r} 5 \\ +\ 5 \\ \hline \end{array}
\qquad
\begin{array}{r} 5 \\ +\ 6 \\ \hline \end{array}
\qquad
\begin{array}{r} 8 \\ -\ 4 \\ \hline \end{array}
\qquad
\begin{array}{r} 7 \\ +\ 8 \\ \hline \end{array}
$$

$$
\begin{array}{r} 9 \\ +\ 8 \\ \hline \end{array}
\qquad
\begin{array}{r} 7 \\ +\ 6 \\ \hline \end{array}
\qquad
\begin{array}{r} 18 \\ -\ 9 \\ \hline \end{array}
\qquad
\begin{array}{r} 8 \\ +\ 7 \\ \hline \end{array}
\qquad
\begin{array}{r} 5 \\ +\ 4 \\ \hline \end{array}
\qquad
\begin{array}{r} 16 \\ -\ 8 \\ \hline \end{array}
\qquad
\begin{array}{r} 2 \\ +\ 3 \\ \hline \end{array}
$$

$$
\begin{array}{r} 8 \\ +\ 7 \\ \hline \end{array}
\qquad
\begin{array}{r} 4 \\ +\ 4 \\ \hline \end{array}
\qquad
\begin{array}{r} 6 \\ +\ 5 \\ \hline \end{array}
\qquad
\begin{array}{r} 8 \\ +\ 8 \\ \hline \end{array}
\qquad
\begin{array}{r} 4 \\ -\ 2 \\ \hline \end{array}
\qquad
\begin{array}{r} 7 \\ +\ 8 \\ \hline \end{array}
\qquad
\begin{array}{r} 6 \\ +\ 7 \\ \hline \end{array}
$$

Two Plus Two Is Not Five, Easy Methods To Learn Addition and Subtraction

Name _____

Practice **Double +1**, **Zero**, and **Right Next to Each Other**.

7 + 6	6 − 5	2 + 3	9 − 8	8 + 7	3 + 4	7 + 8
5 − 4	6 − 6	8 + 7	5 + 6	7 − 6	5 + 4	0 + 8
4 + 3	8 − 7	4 + 5	3 + 0	4 − 3	6 + 5	7 + 6
3 − 2	7 + 8	10 − 9	5 − 0	6 + 7	3 + 2	4 − 4

Practice **Double +1** and **Number Family 4•5•9**.

8 + 7	6 + 7	5 + 4	9 − 5	3 + 4	9 − 4	7 + 8
9 − 5	6 + 5	2 + 3	4 + 5	9 − 5	7 + 6	9 − 4
4 + 3	7 + 8	5 + 6	9 − 4	7 + 8	8 + 9	6 + 5
6 + 7	9 − 5	8 + 7	7 + 6	3 + 2	9 − 4	8 + 7

Name _____

Practice **Double +1**, **Straight Lines**, and **Count by 3s**.

5 + 4	4 + 7	9 − 3	7 + 6	11 − 4	3 + 6	11 − 7
8 + 7	6 + 3	5 + 6	7 + 8	3 + 6	9 − 6	7 + 4
11 − 7	4 + 3	7 + 8	9 − 3	4 + 7	7 + 8	9 − 6
2 + 3	6 + 7	7 + 4	6 + 3	8 + 7	6 + 5	11 − 4

Practice **Double +1**, **Number in the Middle**, and **Curvy Numbers**.

7 + 8	7 + 5	13 − 5	8 − 3	6 + 8	8 + 7	5 + 3
13 − 8	5 + 6	8 + 7	8 + 5	4 + 6	3 + 2	7 + 6
8 + 6	8 − 5	5 + 8	5 + 7	7 + 8	8 − 3	4 + 5
6 + 4	3 + 4	6 + 7	3 + 5	13 − 5	8 + 7	6 + 5

Two Plus Two Is Not Five, Easy Methods To Learn Addition and Subtraction

Name _____

Cumulative Practice. Mark $\rangle$ **Double +1**.

| 5 $+ 6$ | 7 $+ 8$ | 6 $+ 2$ | 6 $+ 7$ | 10 $- 5$ | 3 $+ 6$ | 3 $- 2$ |

| 13 $- 5$ | 8 $- 5$ | 3 $+ 4$ | 11 $- 7$ | 7 $+ 6$ | 2 $- 1$ | 9 $+ 6$ |

| 7 $+ 7$ | 16 $- 7$ | 8 $+ 7$ | 18 $- 9$ | 4 $+ 5$ | 6 $+ 7$ | 12 $- 6$ |

| 4 $+ 7$ | 12 $- 9$ | 8 $- 5$ | 7 $+ 6$ | 8 $+ 9$ | 9 $- 6$ | 5 $+ 4$ |

16−8= _____   7+8= _____   13−9= _____   2+6= _____

3+3= _____   7−7= _____   11−4= _____   6+7= _____

7+6= _____   9−4= _____   5+8= _____   9−3= _____

6+5= _____   7+4= _____   2+3= _____   8+7= _____

8−0= _____   7−3= _____   8+5= _____   6+5= _____

9+1= _____   13−8= _____   6−2= _____   8−3= _____

5+7= _____   5−3= _____   6+4= _____   6+8= _____

Two Plus Two Is Not Five, Easy Methods To Learn Addition and Subtraction

Name _____

TRICK Family Pair

Learn $\begin{array}{r} 7 \\ +2 \\ \hline 9 \end{array}$ $\begin{array}{r} 2 \\ +7 \\ \hline 9 \end{array}$ Think of nose shapes.

$\begin{array}{r} 7 \\ +2 \\ \hline \end{array}$ $\begin{array}{r} 2 \\ +2 \\ \hline \end{array}$ $\begin{array}{r} 2 \\ +7 \\ \hline \end{array}$ $\begin{array}{r} 7 \\ +2 \\ \hline \end{array}$ $\begin{array}{r} 7 \\ +7 \\ \hline \end{array}$ $\begin{array}{r} 2 \\ +7 \\ \hline \end{array}$ $\begin{array}{r} 9 \\ +9 \\ \hline \end{array}$

$\begin{array}{r} 2 \\ +7 \\ \hline \end{array}$ $\begin{array}{r} 7 \\ +7 \\ \hline \end{array}$ $\begin{array}{r} 7 \\ +2 \\ \hline \end{array}$ $\begin{array}{r} 2 \\ +7 \\ \hline \end{array}$ $\begin{array}{r} 9 \\ +9 \\ \hline \end{array}$ $\begin{array}{r} 7 \\ +2 \\ \hline \end{array}$ $\begin{array}{r} 2 \\ +7 \\ \hline \end{array}$

$\begin{array}{r} 9 \\ +9 \\ \hline \end{array}$ $\begin{array}{r} 7 \\ +2 \\ \hline \end{array}$ $\begin{array}{r} 2 \\ +2 \\ \hline \end{array}$ $\begin{array}{r} 7 \\ +2 \\ \hline \end{array}$ $\begin{array}{r} 2 \\ +7 \\ \hline \end{array}$ $\begin{array}{r} 7 \\ +7 \\ \hline \end{array}$ $\begin{array}{r} 7 \\ +2 \\ \hline \end{array}$

Practice **Family Pair** and **Doubles**.

$\begin{array}{r} 2 \\ +7 \\ \hline \end{array}$ $\begin{array}{r} 3 \\ +3 \\ \hline \end{array}$ $\begin{array}{r} 7 \\ +2 \\ \hline \end{array}$ $\begin{array}{r} 8 \\ +8 \\ \hline \end{array}$ $\begin{array}{r} 2 \\ +7 \\ \hline \end{array}$ $\begin{array}{r} 12 \\ -6 \\ \hline \end{array}$ $\begin{array}{r} 4 \\ -2 \\ \hline \end{array}$

$\begin{array}{r} 18 \\ -9 \\ \hline \end{array}$ $\begin{array}{r} 7 \\ +2 \\ \hline \end{array}$ $\begin{array}{r} 6 \\ +6 \\ \hline \end{array}$ $\begin{array}{r} 2 \\ +7 \\ \hline \end{array}$ $\begin{array}{r} 6 \\ -3 \\ \hline \end{array}$ $\begin{array}{r} 7 \\ +2 \\ \hline \end{array}$ $\begin{array}{r} 2 \\ +7 \\ \hline \end{array}$

$\begin{array}{r} 5 \\ +5 \\ \hline \end{array}$ $\begin{array}{r} 14 \\ -7 \\ \hline \end{array}$ $\begin{array}{r} 2 \\ +7 \\ \hline \end{array}$ $\begin{array}{r} 4 \\ +4 \\ \hline \end{array}$ $\begin{array}{r} 2 \\ +7 \\ \hline \end{array}$ $\begin{array}{r} 16 \\ -8 \\ \hline \end{array}$ $\begin{array}{r} 7 \\ +2 \\ \hline \end{array}$

$\begin{array}{r} 8 \\ -4 \\ \hline \end{array}$ $\begin{array}{r} 2 \\ +2 \\ \hline \end{array}$ $\begin{array}{r} 10 \\ -5 \\ \hline \end{array}$ $\begin{array}{r} 7 \\ +2 \\ \hline \end{array}$ $\begin{array}{r} 9 \\ +9 \\ \hline \end{array}$ $\begin{array}{r} 2 \\ +7 \\ \hline \end{array}$ $\begin{array}{r} 7 \\ +7 \\ \hline \end{array}$

Two Plus Two Is Not Five, Easy Methods To Learn Addition and Subtraction

Name _____

Practice **Family Pair** and **Number in the Middle**.

2 + 7	8 + 6	7 + 2	3 + 5	4 + 6	2 + 7	2 + 4
5 + 7	7 + 2	2 + 7	6 + 8	2 + 7	7 + 5	7 + 2
7 + 2	6 + 4	4 + 2	7 + 2	5 + 3	2 + 7	5 + 7

Practice **Family Pair** and **Big Subtraction**.

7 + 2	2 + 7	14 − 5	11 − 9	7 + 2	13 − 9	2 + 7
16 − 9	2 + 7	13 − 9	7 + 2	18 − 9	12 − 3	7 + 2
17 − 9	15 − 6	11 − 2	2 + 7	12 − 9	7 + 2	15 − 9
2 + 7	17 − 8	7 + 2	13 − 9	2 + 7	17 − 9	13 − 4
12 − 9	7 + 2	16 − 7	14 − 9	15 − 6	11 − 9	2 + 7

Two Plus Two Is Not Five, Easy Methods To Learn Addition and Subtraction

Name _____

TRICK Family Partners

You know   7 and   2   Learn   9   9
          + 2   + 7   − 7   − 2
          ———   ———   ———   ———
           9   9   2   7

Look at   9   This **Looks Like** Number in the Middle.
         ····
         − 7
         ————   So the answer = **2**
              ←————

Look at **9−2**.

What number is missing from the family?   2 + _____ = 9

Think of the nose shapes. 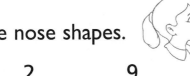 **2   2   9**

7	2	9	7	7	9	9
+ 2	+ 9	− 2	+ 2	+ 9	− 7	− 2

2	9	7	9	2	9	9
+ 7	− 7	+ 9	− 7	+ 7	− 2	− 7

Practice **Number Family** and **Magic 9**. Mark — **Looks Like Number in the Middle.**

9	9	9	8	2	9	9
− 7	+ 7	− 2	+ 9	+ 7	− 7	+ 2

9	7	6	9	9	9	2
+ 3	+ 2	+ 9	− 7	− 2	+ 5	+ 7

4	9	9	5	9	7	9
+ 9	− 2	+ 9	+ 9	− 7	+ 2	− 2

Name _____

Practice **Number Family 2•7•9** and **Zero**.

7 + 2	9 − 2	3 + 0	9 − 7	2 + 7	9 − 9	0 + 7

9 − 7	6 + 0	9 − 2	7 + 2	2 − 0	7 − 0	2 + 7

0 + 9	7 + 2	2 + 7	8 − 0	9 − 2	9 − 7	5 − 5

Practice **Number Family** and **Backwards 1**.

9 − 2	5 − 1	9 − 7	7 − 1	7 + 2	10 − 1	9 − 2

9 − 7	7 + 2	9 − 1	2 + 7	4 − 1	2 + 7	2 − 1

Practice **Number Family** and **Count by 3s**.

2 + 7	9 − 3	3 + 6	9 − 2	6 + 3	9 − 7	3 + 6

6 + 3	9 − 6	9 − 7	2 + 7	9 − 3	7 + 2	9 − 2

7 + 2	9 − 7	3 + 6	9 − 3	2 + 7	9 − 2	9 − 6

Name _____

Practice **Number Families 2•7•9** and **4•5•9**.

2 + 7	9 − 2	4 + 5	9 − 5	9 − 2	9 − 4	5 + 4
9 − 7	9 − 4	7 + 2	9 − 2	9 − 7	9 − 5	9 − 7
9 − 5	2 + 7	9 − 2	5 + 4	9 − 2	9 − 7	9 − 4
4 + 5	9 − 2	7 + 2	9 − 7	9 − 5	4 + 5	2 + 7

Practice **Number Family** and **Straight Lines**.

9 − 7	7 + 4	2 + 7	9 − 2	7 + 2	11 − 7	4 + 7
11 − 4	9 − 2	11 − 7	2 + 7	9 − 7	9 − 2	7 + 2
4 + 7	11 − 7	9 − 7	11 − 4	2 + 7	7 + 4	9 − 7
7 + 2	7 + 4	9 − 2	11 − 7	4 + 7	2 + 7	11 − 4

Two Plus Two Is Not Five, Easy Methods To Learn Addition and Subtraction

Name _____

Practice **Number Family** and **Curvy Numbers**.

9 − 2	5 + 8	2 + 7	13 − 5	7 + 2	5 + 3	13 − 8
8 − 3	3 + 5	9 − 7	2 + 7	13 − 8	9 − 2	8 − 5
8 + 5	9 − 7	13 − 5	5 + 8	8 − 3	8 − 5	7 + 2

Cumulative Practice.

8 + 6	14 − 9	6 + 3	7 + 2	8 + 8	4 + 6	8 + 5
7 − 4	8 + 2	10 − 1	5 − 2	11 − 4	4 + 3	9 − 4

10−2= _____   9−7= _____   7+5= _____   6+9= _____

8−3= _____   11−7= _____   14−7= _____   7+2= _____

9−8= _____   8−4= _____   9−6= _____   5+7= _____

13−4= _____   3−3= _____   7+4= _____   11−2= _____

2+7= _____   6+8= _____   8+1= _____   5−0= _____

Name _____

TRICK Lots of 4s

Learn
$$\begin{array}{r} 4 \\ + 8 \\ \hline 12 \end{array} \qquad \begin{array}{r} 8 \\ + 4 \\ \hline 12 \end{array}$$

$$\boxed{\begin{array}{c} 4 \\ \hline 4 \end{array}} \quad \mathbf{8}$$

$$\boxed{4} \begin{array}{r} + 4 \\ \hline 12 \end{array}$$

Try.

$$\begin{array}{r} 8 \\ + 4 \\ \hline \end{array} \qquad \begin{array}{r} 4 \\ + 4 \\ \hline \end{array} \qquad \begin{array}{r} 4 \\ + 8 \\ \hline \end{array} \qquad \begin{array}{r} 8 \\ + \\ \hline 12 \end{array} \qquad \begin{array}{r} 4 \\ + 8 \\ \hline \end{array} \qquad \begin{array}{r} 4 \\ + 4 \\ \hline \end{array} \qquad \begin{array}{r} 8 \\ + 4 \\ \hline \end{array}$$

$$\begin{array}{r} 4 \\ + \\ \hline 12 \end{array} \qquad \begin{array}{r} 8 \\ + 4 \\ \hline \end{array} \qquad \begin{array}{r} 8 \\ + 8 \\ \hline \end{array} \qquad \begin{array}{r} 8 \\ + 4 \\ \hline \end{array} \qquad \begin{array}{r} 4 \\ + 4 \\ \hline \end{array} \qquad \begin{array}{r} 8 \\ + 4 \\ \hline \end{array} \qquad \begin{array}{r} 4 \\ + 8 \\ \hline \end{array}$$

Practice these.

$$\begin{array}{r} 8 \\ + 4 \\ \hline \end{array} \qquad \begin{array}{r} 5 \\ + 5 \\ \hline \end{array} \qquad \begin{array}{r} 8 \\ + 4 \\ \hline \end{array} \qquad \begin{array}{r} 4 \\ + 8 \\ \hline \end{array} \qquad \begin{array}{r} 8 \\ + 4 \\ \hline \end{array} \qquad \begin{array}{r} 6 \\ + 1 \\ \hline \end{array} \qquad \begin{array}{r} 4 \\ + 8 \\ \hline \end{array}$$

$$\begin{array}{r} 10 \\ - 5 \\ \hline \end{array} \qquad \begin{array}{r} 4 \\ + 8 \\ \hline \end{array} \qquad \begin{array}{r} 1 \\ + 8 \\ \hline \end{array} \qquad \begin{array}{r} 4 \\ + 4 \\ \hline \end{array} \qquad \begin{array}{r} 6 \\ + 6 \\ \hline \end{array} \qquad \begin{array}{r} 8 \\ + 4 \\ \hline \end{array} \qquad \begin{array}{r} 14 \\ - 7 \\ \hline \end{array}$$

$$\begin{array}{r} 4 \\ + 8 \\ \hline \end{array} \qquad \begin{array}{r} 8 \\ + 8 \\ \hline \end{array} \qquad \begin{array}{r} 4 \\ - 4 \\ \hline \end{array} \qquad \begin{array}{r} 7 \\ + 7 \\ \hline \end{array} \qquad \begin{array}{r} 8 \\ + 4 \\ \hline \end{array} \qquad \begin{array}{r} 1 \\ + 4 \\ \hline \end{array} \qquad \begin{array}{r} 8 \\ + 4 \\ \hline \end{array}$$

$$\begin{array}{r} 8 \\ + 4 \\ \hline \end{array} \qquad \begin{array}{r} 4 \\ + 4 \\ \hline \end{array} \qquad \begin{array}{r} 4 \\ + 8 \\ \hline \end{array} \qquad \begin{array}{r} 8 \\ + 4 \\ \hline \end{array} \qquad \begin{array}{r} 8 \\ - 1 \\ \hline \end{array} \qquad \begin{array}{r} 4 \\ + 8 \\ \hline \end{array} \qquad \begin{array}{r} 16 \\ - 8 \\ \hline \end{array}$$

Name _____

Practice **Lots of 4s** and **Right Next to Each Other**.

4 + 8	5 − 4	8 + 4	8 − 7	4 − 3	4 + 8	6 − 5
10 − 9	8 + 4	7 − 6	4 + 8	8 + 4	3 − 2	4 + 8
8 + 4	3 − 2	9 − 8	4 + 8	10 − 9	8 + 4	7 − 6

Practice **Lots of 4s** and **Doubles**.

8 + 4	8 + 8	3 + 3	4 + 8	2 + 2	12 − 6	8 + 4
1 + 1	4 + 8	8 + 4	7 + 7	18 − 9	8 + 4	4 + 8
4 + 8	10 − 5	4 + 4	8 + 4	6 − 3	4 + 8	8 + 8
16 − 8	4 + 8	4 − 2	14 − 7	8 + 4	5 + 5	4 + 8
8 + 4	9 + 9	8 − 4	4 + 8	4 + 4	8 + 4	6 + 6

Name _____

TRICK   Lots of 4s Subtraction

You know   8   and   4   Learn   **12**   **12**
$$+ 4$$ $$+ 8$$ $$- 4$$ $$- 8$$
$$\overline{12}$$ $$\overline{12}$$ $$\overline{8}$$ $$\overline{4}$$

8	4	8	4	12	12	4
$+4$	$+$	$+4$	$+$	-4	-8	$+8$
	$\overline{12}$		$\overline{12}$			

8	12	4	12	8	12	12
$+$	-8	$+8$	-8	$+4$	-4	-8
$\overline{12}$						

Practice **Lots of 4s** and **Count by 3s**.

4	12	9	3	12	6	8
$+8$	-8	-3	$+6$	-8	$+3$	$+4$

12	9	12	6	9	4	12
-4	-6	-8	$+3$	-3	$+8$	-4

9	3	12	12	8	9	4
-3	$+6$	-4	-8	$+4$	-6	$+8$

12	8	9	3	12	12	6
-8	$+4$	-6	$+6$	-4	-8	$+3$

Two Plus Two Is Not Five, Easy Methods To Learn Addition and Subtraction   **155**

Name _____

Practice **Lots of 4s** and **Curvy Numbers**. (Circle) **Lots of 4s**.

12 − 8	8 + 5	13 − 8	4 + 8	8 + 4	8 − 3	12 − 4
5 + 8	8 − 3	12 − 4	8 − 5	12 − 8	5 + 8	13 − 5
4 + 8	8 + 5	3 + 5	12 − 8	8 + 4	12 − 4	8 − 3
12 − 4	8 − 5	8 + 4	13 − 8	12 − 8	4 + 8	5 + 3

Practice **Lots of 4s** and **Number in the Middle**.

12 − 4	8 + 4	7 + 5	6 + 8	12 − 8	4 + 6	8 + 6
3 + 5	12 − 8	8 + 4	5 + 7	6 + 4	12 − 4	4 + 8
4 + 8	6 + 8	12 − 4	5 + 3	12 − 8	8 + 4	8 + 6
12 − 8	4 + 2	4 + 6	4 + 8	9 + 7	7 + 5	8 + 4

Two Plus Two Is Not Five, Easy Methods To Learn Addition and Subtraction

Name _____

Practice **Lots of 4s** and **Straight Lines**.

4 + 8	12 − 8	8 + 4	12 − 4	4 + 7	11 − 7	4 + 8
7 + 4	11 − 7	12 − 4	8 + 4	12 − 4	4 + 7	11 − 4
12 − 8	11 − 4	4 + 7	11 − 7	8 + 4	12 − 8	11 − 7
11 − 4	12 − 4	12 − 8	4 + 7	11 − 4	4 + 8	7 + 4

Practice **Lots of 4s** and **Big Subtraction**.

8 + 4	11 − 9	12 − 8	16 − 9	15 − 6	12 − 4	13 − 9
17 − 8	4 + 8	12 − 4	4 + 8	14 − 9	11 − 2	16 − 7
12 − 8	14 − 5	8 + 4	13 − 4	12 − 3	8 + 4	12 − 4
18 − 9	12 − 4	12 − 8	15 − 9	12 − 8	12 − 9	4 + 8

Two Plus Two Is Not Five, Easy Methods To Learn Addition and Subtraction   **157**

Name _____

Cumulative Practice.

| $\begin{array}{r}12\\-3\\\hline\end{array}$ | $\begin{array}{r}3\\+3\\\hline\end{array}$ | $\begin{array}{r}4\\+8\\\hline\end{array}$ | $\begin{array}{r}13\\-8\\\hline\end{array}$ | $\begin{array}{r}3\\+4\\\hline\end{array}$ | $\begin{array}{r}7\\+4\\\hline\end{array}$ | $\begin{array}{r}6\\+6\\\hline\end{array}$ |

| $\begin{array}{r}6\\-2\\\hline\end{array}$ | $\begin{array}{r}8\\+8\\\hline\end{array}$ | $\begin{array}{r}3\\+2\\\hline\end{array}$ | $\begin{array}{r}9\\+8\\\hline\end{array}$ | $\begin{array}{r}12\\-8\\\hline\end{array}$ | $\begin{array}{r}5\\+7\\\hline\end{array}$ | $\begin{array}{r}3\\+6\\\hline\end{array}$ |

| $\begin{array}{r}9\\-5\\\hline\end{array}$ | $\begin{array}{r}14\\-5\\\hline\end{array}$ | $\begin{array}{r}3\\+9\\\hline\end{array}$ | $\begin{array}{r}5\\+8\\\hline\end{array}$ | $\begin{array}{r}6\\+4\\\hline\end{array}$ | $\begin{array}{r}7\\+7\\\hline\end{array}$ | $\begin{array}{r}8\\+4\\\hline\end{array}$ |

| $\begin{array}{r}11\\-4\\\hline\end{array}$ | $\begin{array}{r}6\\+8\\\hline\end{array}$ | $\begin{array}{r}9\\-9\\\hline\end{array}$ | $\begin{array}{r}5\\+3\\\hline\end{array}$ | $\begin{array}{r}6\\-5\\\hline\end{array}$ | $\begin{array}{r}0\\+7\\\hline\end{array}$ | $\begin{array}{r}8\\-5\\\hline\end{array}$ |

| $\begin{array}{r}4\\+8\\\hline\end{array}$ | $\begin{array}{r}16\\-9\\\hline\end{array}$ | $\begin{array}{r}12\\-4\\\hline\end{array}$ | $\begin{array}{r}5\\-3\\\hline\end{array}$ | $\begin{array}{r}7\\+4\\\hline\end{array}$ | $\begin{array}{r}16\\-8\\\hline\end{array}$ | $\begin{array}{r}18\\-9\\\hline\end{array}$ |

1+6= _____   7+5= _____   12−4= _____   13−5= _____

7−3= _____   8−4= _____   4+5= _____   4+8= _____

8+5= _____   6+2= _____   11−7= _____   9−6= _____

14−7= _____   9−4= _____   8−2= _____   6−0= _____

17−9= _____   9−1= _____   4+2= _____   8+4= _____

5+5= _____   12−8= _____   8−3= _____   9+2= _____

Name _____

TRICK Family Pair

Learn $\begin{array}{r} 5 \\ + 2 \\ \hline 7 \end{array}$ and $\begin{array}{r} 2 \\ + 5 \\ \hline 7 \end{array}$

$2 \vartriangleright 7 \atop 5$ ____ + ____ = 7

____ + ____ = 7

Practice.

5 + 2	5 + 5	2 + 5	5 + 2	2 + 2	2 + 5	7 + 1
2 + 5	7 + 7	5 + 2	2 + 5	4 + 1	5 + 2	2 + 5
2 + 2	5 + 2	2 + 5	1 + 2	2 + 5	5 + 5	5 + 2

Practice **Family Pair** and **Big Subtraction**.

2 + 5	13 − 4	5 + 2	16 − 9	2 + 5	12 − 9	14 − 5
11 − 9	5 + 2	15 − 6	2 + 5	17 − 8	5 + 2	2 + 5
5 + 5	14 − 9	2 + 5	11 − 2	2 + 5	16 − 7	5 + 2
13 − 9	2 + 2	12 − 3	5 + 2	15 − 9	2 + 5	17 − 9

Two Plus Two Is Not Five, Easy Methods To Learn Addition and Subtraction

Name _____

Practice **Family Pair** and **Straight Lines**.

2 + 5	4 + 7	5 + 2	11 − 7	11 − 4	2 + 5	7 + 4
4 + 7	5 + 2	2 + 5	7 + 4	2 + 5	11 − 7	5 + 2
5 + 2	11 − 4	4 + 7	5 + 2	7 + 4	2 + 5	11 − 4

Practice **Family Pair**, **Magic 9**, and **Number +1**.

5 + 2	2 + 5	9 + 5	1 + 2	5 + 2	3 + 9	2 + 5
8 + 1	5 + 2	8 + 9	5 + 2	4 + 9	1 + 6	5 + 2
9 + 7	1 + 7	9 + 1	2 + 5	3 + 1	5 + 2	9 + 2
2 + 5	6 + 9	5 + 2	1 + 4	2 + 5	9 + 4	2 + 1
1 + 9	2 + 5	7 + 9	5 + 2	9 + 8	5 + 1	2 + 5

Name _____

TRICK Family Partners

You know $\begin{array}{r} 5 \\ +2 \\ \hline 7 \end{array}$ and $\begin{array}{r} 2 \\ +5 \\ \hline 7 \end{array}$ Learn $\begin{array}{r} 7 \\ -5 \\ \hline 2 \end{array}$ $\begin{array}{r} 7 \\ -2 \\ \hline 5 \end{array}$

Look at $\begin{array}{r} 7 \\ \cdots \\ -5 \end{array}$ This **Looks Like** Number in the Middle.

$\longleftarrow$ ———— So the answer = **2**

Look at **7−2**.

What number is missing from the family? $2 + \underline{\hspace{1cm}} = 7$

Practice **Number Family**, **Count by 3s**, and **Right Next to Each Other**.

Mark — **Looks Like Number in the Middle**.

$\begin{array}{r} 5 \\ +2 \\ \hline \end{array}$	$\begin{array}{r} 2 \\ + \\ \hline 7 \end{array}$	$\begin{array}{r} 2 \\ +5 \\ \hline \end{array}$	$\begin{array}{r} 7 \\ -2 \\ \hline \end{array}$	$\begin{array}{r} 5 \\ +2 \\ \hline \end{array}$	$\begin{array}{r} 5 \\ + \\ \hline 7 \end{array}$	$\begin{array}{r} 7 \\ -5 \\ \hline \end{array}$
$\begin{array}{r} 2 \\ + \\ \hline 7 \end{array}$	$\begin{array}{r} 7 \\ -5 \\ \hline \end{array}$	$\begin{array}{r} 6 \\ +3 \\ \hline \end{array}$	$\begin{array}{r} 5 \\ + \\ \hline 7 \end{array}$	$\begin{array}{r} 7 \\ -2 \\ \hline \end{array}$	$\begin{array}{r} 9 \\ -8 \\ \hline \end{array}$	$\begin{array}{r} 5 \\ -4 \\ \hline \end{array}$
$\begin{array}{r} 7 \\ -2 \\ \hline \end{array}$	$\begin{array}{r} 9 \\ -3 \\ \hline \end{array}$	$\begin{array}{r} 7 \\ -5 \\ \hline \end{array}$	$\begin{array}{r} 6 \\ -5 \\ \hline \end{array}$	$\begin{array}{r} 6 \\ +3 \\ \hline \end{array}$	$\begin{array}{r} 9 \\ -6 \\ \hline \end{array}$	$\begin{array}{r} 2 \\ +5 \\ \hline \end{array}$
$\begin{array}{r} 7 \\ -5 \\ \hline \end{array}$	$\begin{array}{r} 4 \\ -3 \\ \hline \end{array}$	$\begin{array}{r} 8 \\ -7 \\ \hline \end{array}$	$\begin{array}{r} 9 \\ -3 \\ \hline \end{array}$	$\begin{array}{r} 7 \\ -2 \\ \hline \end{array}$	$\begin{array}{r} 5 \\ +2 \\ \hline \end{array}$	$\begin{array}{r} 3 \\ +6 \\ \hline \end{array}$

Two Plus Two Is Not Five, Easy Methods To Learn Addition and Subtraction

Name _____

Practice **Number Family 2•5•7**, **Curvy Numbers**, and **Backwards 1**.

7 − 2	9 − 1	7 − 5	8 + 5	2 + 5	10 − 1	5 + 2

8 − 3	5 + 2	13 − 8	7 − 5	7 − 2	5 − 1	2 + 5

3 − 1	5 + 8	7 − 2	8 − 5	7 − 5	5 + 2	7 − 1

13 − 5	2 + 5	8 − 3	7 − 2	8 + 5	8 − 1	13 − 8

Practice **Number Family** and **Doubles**.

7 − 5	9 + 9	10 − 5	5 + 2	2 + 5	2 + 2	7 − 2

5 + 2	8 + 8	7 − 2	12 − 6	7 − 5	2 + 5	7 + 7

16 − 8	2 + 5	8 − 4	7 − 5	5 + 5	7 − 2	5 + 2

6 + 6	7 − 2	2 + 5	18 − 9	7 − 5	14 − 7	6 − 3

Name _____

Practice **Number Family** and **Number in the Middle**.

5 + 2	4 + 6	8 + 6	7 − 2	5 + 3	7 + 5	7 − 5

7 − 2	5 + 7	7 − 5	2 + 5	6 + 8	3 + 5	5 + 2

2 + 4	9 + 7	2 + 5	7 + 5	5 + 2	7 − 2	6 + 4

7 − 5	4 + 2	7 − 2	8 + 6	5 + 7	2 + 5	5 + 3

Practice **Number Families 2•5•7**, **4•5•9**, and **Zero**.

7 − 2	5 + 2	9 − 4	1 + 0	5 + 4	4 − 4	9 − 5

0 + 9	6 − 0	7 − 2	9 − 5	2 + 5	3 + 0	7 − 5

7 − 5	9 − 4	4 + 5	7 − 5	7 − 7	5 + 2	8 − 0

2 + 5	9 − 5	5 + 2	9 − 4	7 − 2	0 + 4	4 + 5

Two Plus Two Is Not Five, Easy Methods To Learn Addition and Subtraction **163**

Name _____

Cumulative Practice.

7 − 5	16 − 8	9 − 4	9 + 1	3 + 4	11 − 7	2 + 5

8 + 5	14 − 9	7 − 2	6 + 4	9 − 3	9 + 4	4 − 4

5 + 2	7 + 4	5 + 3	15 − 9	7 − 5	5 + 7	9 − 5

8 + 2	7 − 3	2 + 5	6 + 8	8 − 7	5 − 2	18 − 9

17 − 8	5 − 1	4 + 5	6 − 2	4 + 7	7 − 2	7 + 9

7−4= _____   13−5= _____   3+6= _____   14−7= _____

4+9= _____   3+2= _____   8+8= _____   8−3= _____

5+2= _____   11−9= _____   5−4= _____   7+5= _____

11−4= _____   9−6= _____   13−8= _____   2+6= _____

7−5= _____   6−3= _____   8+6= _____   12−6= _____

5+8= _____   16−7= _____   2+5= _____   9+7= _____

Name _____

TRICK <u>Stretch</u>

Learn $\begin{array}{r} 7 \\ + 3 \\ \hline 10 \end{array}$ and $\begin{array}{r} 3 \\ + 7 \\ \hline 10 \end{array}$ **S t r e t c h** your imagination.

S t r e t c h the 7 into a)

$7+3=$ **10**

S t r e t c h the 3 into a ()

Try.

$\begin{array}{r} 3 \\ + 7 \\ \hline 10 \end{array}$ $\begin{array}{r} 7 \\ + 3 \\ \hline \end{array}$ $\begin{array}{r} 3 \\ + 7 \\ \hline \end{array}$ $\begin{array}{r} 3 \\ + \\ \hline 10 \end{array}$ $\begin{array}{r} 7 \\ + 3 \\ \hline \end{array}$ $\begin{array}{r} 7 \\ + \\ \hline 10 \end{array}$ $\begin{array}{r} 3 \\ + 7 \\ \hline \end{array}$

Practice **<u>Stretch</u>**, **<u>Number +1</u>**, and **<u>Backwards 1</u>**.

$\begin{array}{r} 3 \\ + 7 \\ \hline \end{array}$ $\begin{array}{r} 7 \\ - 1 \\ \hline \end{array}$ $\begin{array}{r} 7 \\ + 3 \\ \hline \end{array}$ $\begin{array}{r} 1 \\ + 5 \\ \hline \end{array}$ $\begin{array}{r} 3 \\ + 7 \\ \hline \end{array}$ $\begin{array}{r} 9 \\ - 1 \\ \hline \end{array}$ $\begin{array}{r} 7 \\ + 3 \\ \hline \end{array}$

$\begin{array}{r} 1 \\ + 8 \\ \hline \end{array}$ $\begin{array}{r} 7 \\ + 3 \\ \hline \end{array}$ $\begin{array}{r} 8 \\ - 1 \\ \hline \end{array}$ $\begin{array}{r} 3 \\ + 7 \\ \hline \end{array}$ $\begin{array}{r} 4 \\ - 1 \\ \hline \end{array}$ $\begin{array}{r} 7 \\ + 3 \\ \hline \end{array}$ $\begin{array}{r} 3 \\ - 1 \\ \hline \end{array}$

$\begin{array}{r} 7 \\ + 3 \\ \hline \end{array}$ $\begin{array}{r} 3 \\ + 7 \\ \hline \end{array}$ $\begin{array}{r} 6 \\ + 1 \\ \hline \end{array}$ $\begin{array}{r} 6 \\ - 1 \\ \hline \end{array}$ $\begin{array}{r} 7 \\ + 3 \\ \hline \end{array}$ $\begin{array}{r} 1 \\ + 2 \\ \hline \end{array}$ $\begin{array}{r} 3 \\ + 7 \\ \hline \end{array}$

$\begin{array}{r} 5 \\ - 1 \\ \hline \end{array}$ $\begin{array}{r} 10 \\ - 1 \\ \hline \end{array}$ $\begin{array}{r} 3 \\ + 7 \\ \hline \end{array}$ $\begin{array}{r} 4 \\ + 1 \\ \hline \end{array}$ $\begin{array}{r} 1 \\ + 7 \\ \hline \end{array}$ $\begin{array}{r} 7 \\ + 3 \\ \hline \end{array}$ $\begin{array}{r} 3 \\ + 1 \\ \hline \end{array}$

Two Plus Two Is Not Five, Easy Methods To Learn Addition and Subtraction

Name _____

Practice **S t r e t c h**, **Doubles**, and **Right Next to Each Other**.

7	3	3	5	16	3	5
+ 3	+ 3	+ 7	− 4	− 8	+ 7	+ 5

4	6	14	9	7	8	7
− 3	+ 6	− 7	+ 9	+ 3	− 7	+ 3

18	3	9	3	7	3	6
− 9	+ 7	− 8	− 2	+ 7	+ 7	− 5

10	7	6	3	7	8	8
− 9	+ 3	− 3	+ 7	− 6	− 4	+ 8

Practice **S t r e t c h**, **Straight Lines**, and **Curvy Numbers**.

7+3= _____   4+7= _____   11−7= _____   3+7= _____

11−4= _____   8+5= _____   13−8= _____   7+3= _____

8−3= _____   11−4= _____   7+3= _____   8−5= _____

3+7= _____   7+3= _____   5+8= _____   7+4= _____

13−5= _____   7+4= _____   3+7= _____   5+3= _____

8+5= _____   8−5= _____   4+7= _____   3+7= _____

11−7= _____   7+3= _____   3+5= _____   13−5= _____

166 Two Plus Two Is Not Five, Easy Methods To Learn Addition and Subtraction

Name _____

TRICK Stretch Subtraction

S t r e t c h your imagination.

You know   **3**   and   **7**   Learn   **10**   **10**
            +7   **+3**   **−3**   **−7**
            10   **10**   **7**   **3**

Try.

$$\begin{array}{r} 3 \\ +7 \\ \hline \end{array} \qquad \begin{array}{r} 7 \\ + \\ \hline 10 \end{array} \qquad \begin{array}{r} 10 \\ -7 \\ \hline \end{array} \qquad \begin{array}{r} 3 \\ + \\ \hline 10 \end{array} \qquad \begin{array}{r} 10 \\ -3 \\ \hline \end{array} \qquad \begin{array}{r} 7 \\ +3 \\ \hline \end{array} \qquad \begin{array}{r} 10 \\ -7 \\ \hline \end{array}$$

$$\begin{array}{r} 3 \\ + \\ \hline 10 \end{array} \qquad \begin{array}{r} 10 \\ -3 \\ \hline \end{array} \qquad \begin{array}{r} 7 \\ +3 \\ \hline \end{array} \qquad \begin{array}{r} 10 \\ -7 \\ \hline \end{array} \qquad \begin{array}{r} 10 \\ -3 \\ \hline \end{array} \qquad \begin{array}{r} 10 \\ -7 \\ \hline \end{array} \qquad \begin{array}{r} 3 \\ +7 \\ \hline \end{array}$$

Practice **S t r e t c h** and **Number Family 4•5•9**.

$$\begin{array}{r} 10 \\ -7 \\ \hline \end{array} \qquad \begin{array}{r} 3 \\ +7 \\ \hline \end{array} \qquad \begin{array}{r} 9 \\ -5 \\ \hline \end{array} \qquad \begin{array}{r} 10 \\ -3 \\ \hline \end{array} \qquad \begin{array}{r} 4 \\ +5 \\ \hline \end{array} \qquad \begin{array}{r} 9 \\ -4 \\ \hline \end{array} \qquad \begin{array}{r} 7 \\ +3 \\ \hline \end{array}$$

$$\begin{array}{r} 5 \\ +4 \\ \hline \end{array} \qquad \begin{array}{r} 9 \\ -4 \\ \hline \end{array} \qquad \begin{array}{r} 10 \\ -3 \\ \hline \end{array} \qquad \begin{array}{r} 4 \\ +5 \\ \hline \end{array} \qquad \begin{array}{r} 7 \\ +3 \\ \hline \end{array} \qquad \begin{array}{r} 9 \\ -5 \\ \hline \end{array} \qquad \begin{array}{r} 10 \\ -7 \\ \hline \end{array}$$

$$\begin{array}{r} 3 \\ +7 \\ \hline \end{array} \qquad \begin{array}{r} 9 \\ -5 \\ \hline \end{array} \qquad \begin{array}{r} 5 \\ +4 \\ \hline \end{array} \qquad \begin{array}{r} 10 \\ -3 \\ \hline \end{array} \qquad \begin{array}{r} 3 \\ +7 \\ \hline \end{array} \qquad \begin{array}{r} 10 \\ -7 \\ \hline \end{array} \qquad \begin{array}{r} 9 \\ -4 \\ \hline \end{array}$$

$$\begin{array}{r} 10 \\ -7 \\ \hline \end{array} \qquad \begin{array}{r} 9 \\ -4 \\ \hline \end{array} \qquad \begin{array}{r} 7 \\ +3 \\ \hline \end{array} \qquad \begin{array}{r} 9 \\ -5 \\ \hline \end{array} \qquad \begin{array}{r} 3 \\ +7 \\ \hline \end{array} \qquad \begin{array}{r} 4 \\ +5 \\ \hline \end{array} \qquad \begin{array}{r} 10 \\ -3 \\ \hline \end{array}$$

Name _____

Practice **Stretch**, **Zero**, and **Magic 9**.

10 − 3	9 + 5	10 − 7	3 + 0	7 + 9	3 + 7	7 − 7
10 − 7	0 + 7	9 + 8	10 − 3	4 + 9	9 + 9	7 + 3
3 − 0	1 − 1	7 + 3	9 + 6	3 − 3	10 − 7	2 + 9
3 + 7	10 − 3	9 + 3	7 + 0	10 − 7	0 + 3	10 − 3

Practice **Stretch** and **Number Families 2•3•5** and **3•4•7**.

7 + 3	3 + 2	10 − 3	5 − 3	10 − 3	3 + 4	10 − 7
7 − 4	5 − 2	7 − 3	10 − 7	4 + 3	3 + 7	7 − 4
3 + 2	7 + 3	10 − 3	5 − 3	10 − 7	7 − 3	5 − 3
10 − 7	7 − 3	2 + 3	5 − 2	3 + 4	3 + 7	10 − 3

Two Plus Two Is Not Five, Easy Methods To Learn Addition and Subtraction

Name _____

Practice **Stretch** and **Big Subtraction**.

7 + 3	10 − 3	11 − 2	15 − 9	7 + 3	17 − 8	14 − 5
10 − 7	12 − 9	16 − 7	7 + 3	13 − 9	3 + 7	10 − 3
14 − 9	3 + 7	10 − 3	16 − 9	10 − 7	17 − 9	13 − 4
10 − 7	11 − 9	7 + 3	15 − 6	3 + 7	10 − 3	10 − 7

Practice **Stretch**, **Number in the Middle**, and **Count by 3s**.

3+7= _____   8+6= _____   6+3= _____   9−3= _____

4+6= _____   10−7= _____   9−6= _____   3+5= _____

7+5= _____   3+6= _____   10−3= _____   9−6= _____

6+8= _____   7+3= _____   6+4= _____   10−7= _____

3+6= _____   10−3= _____   3+7= _____   8+6= _____

9−6= _____   5+7= _____   6+4= _____   10−3= _____

7+3= _____   9−3= _____   6+8= _____   7+5= _____

Two Plus Two Is Not Five, Easy Methods To Learn Addition and Subtraction 169

Name _____

Cumulative Practice. (Circle) **Stretch**.

10 − 3	11 − 9	6 + 3	9 + 0	14 − 7	3 + 7	5 + 4
7 − 4	1 − 1	10 − 7	4 + 6	17 − 8	11 − 4	7 + 3
15 − 6	7 + 9	8 − 2	5 + 8	7 + 3	2 + 8	10 − 3
10 − 7	16 − 9	8 − 5	4 − 3	6 + 1	13 − 5	5 + 7
6 + 8	6 − 2	10 − 3	14 − 5	2 + 9	3 + 5	11 − 7
3 + 7	9 − 5	11 − 2	13 − 8	1 + 8	10 − 7	9 + 9
13 − 9	8 + 8	5 + 3	7 + 3	12 − 6	3 + 6	10 − 3
8 + 5	10 − 7	4 + 7	8 + 6	8 − 3	9 − 6	7 + 5

Two Plus Two Is Not Five, Easy Methods To Learn Addition and Subtraction

Name _____

Tiers 1, 2, 3, 4, and 5 Review
Review <u>**Looks Like Number in the Middle**</u> and <u>**Number in the Middle**</u>.

$$
\begin{array}{ccccccc}
8 & 8 & 6 & 7 & 9 & 10 & 5 \\
-6 & +6 & -4 & +5 & -7 & -8 & +7 \\
\end{array}
$$

$$
\begin{array}{ccccccc}
6 & 7 & 6 & 9 & 10 & 5 & 8 \\
-4 & -5 & +8 & -7 & -8 & -3 & -6 \\
\end{array}
$$

$$
\begin{array}{ccccccc}
9 & 6 & 3 & 7 & 8 & 6 & 5 \\
-7 & +4 & +5 & -5 & -6 & +8 & -3 \\
\end{array}
$$

$$
\begin{array}{ccccccc}
4 & 5 & 10 & 5 & 6 & 7 & 4 \\
-2 & +7 & -8 & +3 & -4 & -5 & +6 \\
\end{array}
$$

Review <u>**Looks Like Number in the Middle**</u> and <u>**Straight Lines**</u>.

6−4= _____   11−4= _____   7−5= _____   4+7= _____

9−7= _____   5−3= _____   7+4= _____   11−7= _____

10−8= _____   4+7= _____   4−2= _____   7+4= _____

11−7= _____   8−6= _____   4+7= _____   7−5= _____

5−3= _____   7−5= _____   11−7= _____   9−7= _____

10−8= _____   11−4= _____   6−4= _____   8−6= _____

9−7= _____   7+4= _____   8−6= _____   10−8= _____

Two Plus Two Is Not Five, Easy Methods To Learn Addition and Subtraction   **171**

Name _____

Tiers 1, 2, 3, 4, and 5 Review

Review **<u>Looks Like Number in the Middle</u>**, **<u>Curvy Numbers</u>**, and
<u>Right Next to Each Other</u>.

9 − 7	3 + 5	10 − 8	13 − 8	8 − 6	9 − 8	5 − 3
8 + 5	7 − 5	5 − 4	8 − 5	7 − 6	6 − 4	10 − 8
10 − 9	8 − 3	13 − 5	9 − 7	3 − 2	5 + 8	6 − 5
5 + 3	8 − 6	4 − 3	6 − 4	8 − 7	5 − 3	7 − 5

Review **<u>Looks Like in the Middle</u>**, **<u>Big Subtraction</u>**, and **<u>Number +1</u>**.

10 − 8	13 − 4	5 − 3	12 − 9	1 + 7	14 − 9	9 + 1
12 − 3	9 − 7	1 + 2	6 − 4	15 − 9	17 − 8	8 − 6
1 + 6	7 − 5	17 − 9	5 + 1	16 − 7	12 − 3	8 + 1
10 − 8	11 − 9	13 − 9	14 − 5	4 − 2	1 + 3	11 − 2

Name _____

Tiers 1, 2, 3, 4, and 5 Review
Review **2 Ladder** and **Doubles**.

4 + 2	6 + 6	2 + 8	5 + 5	8 − 6	4 + 4	10 − 8
8 + 8	8 − 2	6 − 4	7 + 7	10 − 5	3 + 3	4 − 2
14 − 7	16 − 8	2 + 2	2 + 6	10 − 2	8 − 4	12 − 6
6 − 4	6 − 3	8 + 2	10 − 8	6 + 2	6 − 2	8 − 6

Review **2 Ladder** and **Stretch**.

2 + 8	6 − 4	10 − 7	7 + 3	8 − 6	10 − 3	6 + 2
3 + 7	2 + 6	10 − 2	8 − 2	10 − 3	2 + 4	10 − 7
10 − 8	7 + 3	10 − 3	8 − 6	10 − 7	8 + 2	6 − 4
7 + 3	10 − 7	4 + 2	3 + 7	6 − 2	10 − 3	3 + 7

Two Plus Two Is Not Five, Easy Methods To Learn Addition and Subtraction **173**

Name _____

Tiers 1, 2, 3, 4, and 5 Review
Review **2 Ladder** and **Lots of 4s**.

8 − 2	6 − 4	12 − 8	10 − 2	8 + 4	2 + 6	12 − 4
2 + 8	2 + 4	12 − 4	4 + 8	6 − 4	6 − 2	10 − 8
12 − 8	8 + 4	8 − 6	12 − 8	2 + 6	12 − 4	8 + 2
4 + 8	6 + 2	4 + 8	10 − 8	8 − 6	8 + 4	4 + 2

Review **2 Ladder** and **Big Subtraction**.

10−8= _____   6+2= _____   17−8= _____   11−2= _____

16−7= _____   13−9= _____   8+2= _____   14−9= _____

8−2= _____   6−2= _____   15−9= _____   8−6= _____

6−4= _____   14−5= _____   2+4= _____   10−2= _____

15−6= _____   16−9= _____   8−6= _____   12−9= _____

4+2= _____   2+8= _____   6−2= _____   17−9= _____

12−3= _____   11−9= _____   13−4= _____   2+6= _____

Two Plus Two Is Not Five, Easy Methods To Learn Addition and Subtraction

Name _____

Tiers 1, 2, 3, 4, and 5 Review
Review **Double +1** and **S t r e t c h**.

6	4	10	7	8	10	6
+ 7	+ 5	− 7	+ 3	+ 7	− 3	+ 5

3	5	7	9	10	2	3
+ 7	+ 6	+ 8	+ 8	− 7	+ 3	+ 7

3	7	10	5	7	8	5
+ 4	+ 6	− 3	+ 6	+ 3	+ 7	+ 4

10	5	4	3	7	10	3
− 7	+ 6	+ 3	+ 7	+ 8	− 3	+ 4

Review **Double +1** and **Magic 9**.

8+7= _____   6+9= _____   4+5= _____   7+6= _____

4+9= _____   8+9= _____   6+7= _____   3+4= _____

9+3= _____   9+7= _____   3+2= _____   6+5= _____

7+8= _____   2+9= _____   5+9= _____   9+9= _____

5+6= _____   3+9= _____   2+3= _____   9+4= _____

9+2= _____   4+3= _____   9+5= _____   7+6= _____

7+9= _____   9+6= _____   5+4= _____   9+8= _____

Two Plus Two Is Not Five, Easy Methods To Learn Addition and Subtraction   **175**

Name _____

Tiers 1, 2, 3, 4, and 5 Review
Review **Double +1**, **Looks Like Number in the Middle**, and **Backwards 1**.

7 + 6	4 + 5	2 − 1	7 − 5	8 − 6	7 + 8	7 − 1
10 − 1	6 − 4	5 − 3	6 + 5	3 + 2	9 − 7	5 + 4
7 − 5	9 − 7	5 − 1	3 + 4	6 − 4	9 − 1	9 − 7
8 − 6	8 + 7	3 − 1	5 − 3	8 − 1	6 + 7	5 + 6

Review **Double +1** and **2 Ladder**.

6+5= _____   7+6= _____   6+2= _____   10−2= _____

6−4= _____   3+4= _____   5+4= _____   7+8= _____

2+8= _____   6−2= _____   6+7= _____   8−6= _____

4+3= _____   8+7= _____   4+2= _____   2+6= _____

10−8= _____   2+3= _____   6−4= _____   8−2= _____

5+6= _____   8−6= _____   8+2= _____   4+5= _____

7+8= _____   10−8= _____   7+6= _____   3+2= _____

Two Plus Two Is Not Five, Easy Methods To Learn Addition and Subtraction

Name _____

Tiers 1, 2, 3, 4, and 5 Review
Review **Number Family 2•7•9** and **Lots of 4s**.

2 + 7	8 + 4	9 − 7	4 + 8	7 + 2	12 − 4	9 − 2
4 + 8	12 − 8	7 + 2	9 − 2	12 − 4	4 + 8	2 + 7
7 + 2	9 − 2	8 + 4	9 − 7	12 − 8	9 − 7	12 − 4

Review **Number Family** and **Looks Like Number in the Middle**.

7 − 5	7 + 2	9 − 7	8 − 6	2 + 7	6 − 4	10 − 8
5 − 3	9 − 2	4 − 2	7 + 2	9 − 7	5 − 3	7 − 5
9 − 2	10 − 8	9 − 7	2 + 7	6 − 4	2 + 7	9 − 2
8 − 6	7 − 5	7 + 2	9 − 7	9 − 2	7 − 5	8 − 6
2 + 7	5 − 3	9 − 2	10 − 8	9 − 7	6 − 4	7 + 2

Name _____

Tiers 1, 2, 3, 4, and 5 Review
Review **Number Family** and **2 Ladder**.

| $\begin{array}{r}9\\-7\\\hline\end{array}$ | $\begin{array}{r}8\\+2\\\hline\end{array}$ | $\begin{array}{r}2\\+7\\\hline\end{array}$ | $\begin{array}{r}9\\-7\\\hline\end{array}$ | $\begin{array}{r}7\\+2\\\hline\end{array}$ | $\begin{array}{r}9\\-2\\\hline\end{array}$ | $\begin{array}{r}10\\-8\\\hline\end{array}$ |

| $\begin{array}{r}10\\-2\\\hline\end{array}$ | $\begin{array}{r}2\\+6\\\hline\end{array}$ | $\begin{array}{r}9\\-7\\\hline\end{array}$ | $\begin{array}{r}2\\+7\\\hline\end{array}$ | $\begin{array}{r}6\\-4\\\hline\end{array}$ | $\begin{array}{r}4\\+2\\\hline\end{array}$ | $\begin{array}{r}9\\-2\\\hline\end{array}$ |

| $\begin{array}{r}9\\-7\\\hline\end{array}$ | $\begin{array}{r}8\\-6\\\hline\end{array}$ | $\begin{array}{r}7\\+2\\\hline\end{array}$ | $\begin{array}{r}6\\-2\\\hline\end{array}$ | $\begin{array}{r}2\\+8\\\hline\end{array}$ | $\begin{array}{r}7\\+2\\\hline\end{array}$ | $\begin{array}{r}6\\+2\\\hline\end{array}$ |

| $\begin{array}{r}6\\-4\\\hline\end{array}$ | $\begin{array}{r}9\\-2\\\hline\end{array}$ | $\begin{array}{r}10\\-8\\\hline\end{array}$ | $\begin{array}{r}9\\-2\\\hline\end{array}$ | $\begin{array}{r}2\\+4\\\hline\end{array}$ | $\begin{array}{r}8\\-6\\\hline\end{array}$ | $\begin{array}{r}2\\+7\\\hline\end{array}$ |

Review **Number Family** and **Double +1**.

2+7= _____	9−7= _____	7+6= _____	5+4= _____
7+8= _____	3+4= _____	9−2= _____	7+2= _____
9−7= _____	5+6= _____	8+7= _____	2+3= _____

7+2= _____	9−2= _____	4+5= _____	2+7= _____
6+7= _____	6+5= _____	9−7= _____	4+3= _____
9−2= _____	8+7= _____	7+2= _____	7+6= _____
8+9= _____	2+7= _____	7+8= _____	3+2= _____

Two Plus Two Is Not Five, Easy Methods To Learn Addition and Subtraction

Name _____

Tiers 1, 2, 3, 4, and 5 Review
Review **Lots of 4s**, **2 Ladder**, and **Straight Lines**.

4 + 8	12 − 8	11 − 4	4 + 8	6 − 4	8 − 2	4 + 7
11 − 7	10 − 2	2 + 6	12 − 4	7 + 4	4 + 8	11 − 7
8 + 4	11 − 4	6 − 2	7 + 4	12 − 8	10 − 8	8 + 4
4 + 7	8 − 6	11 − 7	12 − 8	4 + 7	8 + 2	12 − 4
2 + 4	6 + 2	12 − 4	2 + 8	11 − 4	7 + 4	4 + 8

Review **Lots of 4s** and **Double +1**.

8 + 4	12 − 4	7 + 6	6 + 5	12 − 8	3 + 4	4 + 8
3 + 2	8 + 4	12 − 8	8 + 7	5 + 4	12 − 4	7 + 8
4 + 8	4 + 5	12 − 4	4 + 8	12 − 8	8 + 4	6 + 7

Two Plus Two Is Not Five, Easy Methods To Learn Addition and Subtraction **179**

Name _____

Tiers 1, 2, 3, 4, and 5 Review

Review **Lots of 4s**, **Looks Like Number in the Middle**, and **Zero**.

12 −8	9 −7	0 +5	4 +8	10 −8	6 −4	3 −3
5 −0	8 +4	7 −5	12 −4	0 +1	5 −3	4 +8
8 −6	6 +0	4 +8	4 −4	4 −2	12 −8	2 −0
6 −4	12 −4	9 −7	8 −6	8 +4	7 −5	12 −4

Review **Lots of 4s**, **Big Subtraction**, and **S t r e t c h**.

12 −4	4 +8	7 +3	15 −9	14 −5	10 −3	11 −9
3 +7	12 −9	12 −8	17 −9	8 +4	12 −4	7 +3
16 −7	8 +4	10 −7	12 −8	3 +7	16 −9	15 −6
4 +8	13 −9	12 −4	7 +3	10 −7	8 +4	10 −3

Two Plus Two Is Not Five, Easy Methods To Learn Addition and Subtraction

Name _____

Tiers 1, 2, 3, 4, and 5 Review
Review **Number Family 2•5•7** and **Double +1**.

7 − 2	4 + 3	7 + 6	7 − 5	2 + 5	8 + 7	5 + 6
8 + 7	6 + 7	5 + 2	2 + 3	7 − 5	2 + 5	3 + 4
2 + 5	7 + 8	7 − 2	6 + 7	5 + 2	4 + 5	7 − 2
7 + 6	5 + 4	7 − 5	9 + 8	7 + 8	6 + 5	5 + 2

Review **Number Family**, **2 Ladder**, and **Count by 3s**.

5+2= _____   2+8= _____   7−5= _____   9−3= _____

8−6= _____   10−2= _____   9−6= _____   6+2= _____

6+3= _____   2+5= _____   8−2= _____   7−2= _____

9−3= _____   6−4= _____   2+4= _____   2+5= _____

5+2= _____   7−2= _____   3+6= _____   10−8= _____

8+2= _____   9−6= _____   6−2= _____   7−5= _____

7−2= _____   6+3= _____   2+5= _____   3+6= _____

Two Plus Two Is Not Five, Easy Methods To Learn Addition and Subtraction

Name _____

Tiers 1, 2, 3, 4, and 5 Review
Review **Number Family**, **Backwards 1**, and **Lots of 4s**.

7 − 2	5 − 1	12 − 8	9 − 1	4 + 8	7 − 5	2 + 5
3 − 1	10 − 1	8 + 4	5 + 2	7 − 2	4 + 8	12 − 4
5 + 2	12 − 8	7 − 5	6 − 1	2 + 5	8 + 4	7 − 5
12 − 4	2 + 5	7 − 2	12 − 8	4 − 1	5 + 2	8 + 4

Review **Number Families 2•5•7**, **2•7•9**, and **Big Subtraction**.

2 + 7	9 − 2	2 + 5	7 − 5	13 − 9	7 − 2	17 − 8
12 − 3	5 + 2	7 + 2	15 − 9	9 − 7	14 − 5	9 − 2
7 − 2	2 + 7	16 − 9	9 − 2	12 − 9	7 − 5	9 − 7
13 − 4	17 − 9	5 + 2	11 − 2	7 + 2	16 − 7	2 + 5

Two Plus Two Is Not Five, Easy Methods To Learn Addition and Subtraction

Name _____

Tiers 1, 2, 3, 4, and 5 Review
Review **S t r e t c h** and **Straight Lines**.

7 + 3	11 − 7	3 + 7	10 − 3	7 + 3	4 + 7	11 − 4
10 − 3	7 + 4	10 − 7	7 + 4	10 − 3	11 − 7	3 + 7
4 + 7	7 + 3	11 − 4	11 − 7	4 + 7	7 + 3	10 − 7
7 + 4	10 − 7	3 + 7	10 − 7	11 − 4	11 − 7	4 + 7

Review **S t r e t c h**, **Number Families**, and **Looks Like Number in the Middle**.

10 − 7	9 − 7	2 + 7	10 − 8	8 − 6	10 − 3	5 + 2
7 − 2	3 + 7	9 − 2	5 + 2	5 − 3	7 + 2	7 + 3
7 − 5	6 − 4	10 − 3	3 + 7	7 − 2	9 − 7	10 − 8
2 + 7	7 + 3	2 + 5	9 − 2	10 − 7	7 − 5	6 − 4

Two Plus Two Is Not Five, Easy Methods To Learn Addition and Subtraction

Name _____

Tiers 1, 2, 3, 4, and 5 Review
Review **S t r e t c h** and **Curvy Numbers**.

10 − 7	8 + 5	7 + 3	10 − 3	13 − 8	8 − 5	5 + 8
3 + 7	8 − 5	13 − 5	7 + 3	10 − 3	8 + 5	10 − 7
5 + 8	3 + 7	3 + 5	13 − 8	3 + 7	13 − 5	5 + 3
10 − 3	13 − 5	10 − 7	8 − 5	13 − 8	8 − 3	7 + 3

Review **S t r e t c h** and **Lots of 4s**.

7+3= _____   12−8= _____   4+8= _____   10−3= _____

10−7= _____   3+7= _____   10−3= _____   8+4= _____

8+4= _____   4+8= _____   12−4= _____   3+7= _____

12−4= _____   10−3= _____   7+3= _____   12−8= _____

4+8= _____   7+3= _____   8+4= _____   10−7= _____

12−8= _____   10−7= _____   3+7= _____   12−4= _____

10−3= _____   8+4= _____   10−7= _____   4+8= _____

Two Plus Two Is Not Five, Easy Methods To Learn Addition and Subtraction

Name _____

Tiers 1, 2, 3, 4, and 5 Review
Review all tricks.

11 − 2	9 + 4	3 + 6	9 − 2	14 − 7	7 + 2	10 − 3
12 − 8	8 + 7	8 − 6	3 + 7	7 − 4	14 − 9	6 + 4
5 − 3	6 + 5	10 − 8	5 + 3	6 + 7	7 − 2	4 + 8
9 − 7	5 − 0	13 − 4	9 − 8	11 − 4	8 − 3	16 − 8
5 + 6	8 + 4	10 − 1	6 − 2	2 + 7	9 − 4	8 + 6
2 + 5	7 + 8	5 + 0	8 − 5	12 − 4	2 + 8	4 + 7
9 − 6	13 − 9	7 + 5	9 + 6	8 − 4	7 + 3	6 − 4
7 − 5	10 − 7	5 + 1	5 + 8	11 − 7	13 − 8	7 + 6

Two Plus Two Is Not Five, Easy Methods To Learn Addition and Subtraction **185**

Name _____

Tiers 1, 2, 3, 4, and 5 Review
Review all tricks.

4 + 3	5 − 4	9 + 5	6 + 8	9 − 1	11 − 7	9 − 3
4 + 6	0 + 3	7 − 3	8 + 4	13 − 5	6 + 5	8 + 2
2 + 5	12 − 4	8 + 8	8 − 6	5 + 7	9 + 8	10 − 3
18 − 9	7 + 2	7 + 4	17 − 9	8 + 7	9 − 2	8 + 5
15 − 6	7 + 9	7 − 2	6 + 3	13 − 8	7 + 3	6 + 7
12 − 8	11 − 9	9 − 5	4 + 8	10 − 2	7 − 5	6 − 4
8 − 3	7 + 7	9 − 9	10 − 7	1 + 9	11 − 4	10 − 8
5 + 2	9 − 7	12 − 6	5 + 6	3 + 7	7 + 8	2 + 7

Tier 6

Instructions and Information

Start with any trick. The tricks may be introduced in any order except:

- The three **Big Subtraction Shortcut** sets of facts should be taught in the given sequence, but each set does not have to immediately follow the set before it.

- The **Family Pair** should be taught before the related **Family Partners**, but the subtraction facts do not have to immediately follow the addition facts.

Page	Trick	Math fact cards to be assigned:
187-188	**Big Subtraction Shortcut**	10-4, 10-6
189-192	**Big Subtraction Shortcut**	12-5, 12-7
193-196	**Big Subtraction Shortcut**	14-6, 14-8
197-200	**Family Partners**	11-5, 11-6
201-204	**Family Partners**	13-6, 13-7
205-208	**Family Partners**	15-7, 15-8
209-210	**Family Pair**	3+8, 8+3
211-214	**Family Partners**	11-3, 11-8
215-232	**Review Pages**	

Tier 6 Answers

Page 187
6,10,4,6,5,10,4
10,4,10,4,10,6,9
4,10,6,9,6,10,10
6,4,10,6,10,4,6

Page 188
6,12,3,4,12,4,4
9,6,8,6,6,12,9
6,4,4,9,8,4,6
4,3,12,6,9,4,8
4,12,14,0,8,6,10
8,12,4,6,7,14,12
0,4,4,10,4,6,16
14,0,6,8,9,1,4

Page 189
7,12,5,7,5,12,7
4,5,12,5,12,7,4
5,12,7,6,7,12,5
6,5,4,7,12,4,12

Page 190
5,10,10,7,8,6,6
7,4,7,2,2,5,6
5,5,8,4,10,4,5
6,2,8,4,3,4,8
6,7,6,9,2,7,8
7,11,13,6,8,4,7
8,11,4,5,7,13,3
4,5,5,11,6,8,5

Page 191
7,12,6,8,4,4,5
4,5,8,6,12,4,4
12,6,7,12,8,6,4
8,5,12,4,12,7,12
6,2,5,2,2,2,7
2,7,2,5,4,2,6
2,2,4,2,2,5,2
2,6,2,2,7,4,2

Page 192
5,10,3,7,10,4,7
10,6,5,4,10,7,3
7,10,7,5,6,10,7
4,7,10,6,5,3,10
7,6,2,5
7,9,5,9
4,2,7,7
9,6,4,7
5,5,2,7
7,4,2,9
7,7,5,6

Page 193
8,14,6,8,4,5,6
14,6,7,6,8,10,4
5,4,8,14,5,6,14
6,14,7,8,5,6,6

Page 194
8,6,10,12,5,3,4
14,8,7,4,7,5,6
6,5,8,6,4,8,2
6,16,4,9,2,7,6
7,8,4,13
7,6,15,6
5,11,8,9
4,7,13,11
6,17,5,6
15,6,11,5
9,5,15,8

Page 195
6,3,1,5,3,1,6
1,7,8,1,0,6,5
4,4,1,7,8,1,1
8,5,1,4,7,0,6
4,6,8,9,5,9,8
6,2,6,9,9,9,5
7,7,8,9,3,9,4
6,4,5,6,7,6,9

Page 196
12,6,6,6,6,6,7
10,8,8,6,15,12,4
8,4,13,10,2,3,3
6,5,9,13,5,2,5
13,8,9,11,3,8,14
1,4,9,7,2,7,7
4,2,8,9,4,9,2
10,12,7,5,6,7,5

Page 197
6,5
6,6,11,5,5,11,6
5,11,5,5,6,11,6
6,12,5,6,11,5,11
5,10,6,7,3,5,10
6,3,10,5,10,7,6
10,7,6,10,6,5,3

Page 198
5,6,11,4,11,6,7
11,11,5,11,5,11,4
6,11,4,6,11,7,5
11,7,11,7,5,11,11
11,5,18,5
6,12,5,14
9,8,7,11
16,5,4,3
4,6,8,10
11,2,5,11
6,11,6,6

Page 199
6,2,12,2,5,16,6
2,5,2,6,17,2,5
6,13,11,2,5,2,15
2,14,6,2,2,5,2
11,12,6,2,4,12,2
5,6,11,9,7,8,5
12,4,5,8,9,7,4
5,2,9,5,12,6,2

Page 200
6,15,11,6,5,5,11
5,9,6,7,5,11,13
15,6,13,5,7,17,6
12,6,1,12,6,6,5
5,9,10,7,14,7,17
4,9,4,6,8,12,11
2,4,5,6,3,11,7
11,9,8,10,13,13,5

Page 201
6,7
6,6,7,7,13,6,7
13,7,13,7,7,12,6
7,13,6,7,6,6,13
6,7,6,3
3,7,4,7
7,7,7,4
7,4,3,6
4,6,7,7

Page 202
13,10,6,8,2,13,7
6,7,13,8,13,6,2
7,8,6,6,2,10,13
6,2,6,13,4,7,2
6,8,13,2,7,9,13
13,4,9,7,13,9,6
9,9,13,9,7,13,9
7,6,7,3,13,6,9

Page 203
6,13,7,13,8,6,3
13,7,5,5,7,8,6
7,3,13,8,8,7,5
13,6,8,5,5,6,13
7,8,5,5,2,13,9
2,3,7,7,13,3,2
6,5,9,6,2,6,7
9,3,13,9,6,7,2

Page 204
6,4,8,12,8,12,7
9,6,12,6,6,5,4
7,12,8,6,7,7,3
4,10,7,12,7,8,6
6,10,3,13,7,9,10
9,7,10,7,9,6,6
3,3,7,13,7,10,13
7,9,6,6,10,13,3

Page 205
15,8,8,15,7,8,15
7,8,14,8,7,16,8
10,7,7,15,1,8,7

Page 206
15,5,8,15,8,13,7
9,7,13,17,7,15,7
7,15,11,8,11,5,15
5,7,8,15,13,8,9
8,15,6,5
14,7,9,7
5,9,15,12
9,6,4,8
3,9,16,15
7,9,9,9
3,10,15,7

Page 207
8,2,12,2,7,2,4
2,12,7,2,8,2,8
4,7,2,8,8,7,2
12,2,8,7,12,2,7
7,13,8,7
15,10,12,7
11,18,10,16
3,8,14,10
7,10,7,8
17,3,11,7
7,13,8,3

Page 208
8,9,15,13,6,8,7
3,15,5,9,3,15,8
5,6,7,8,9,5,3
13,8,3,5,8,6,15
12,8,10,7,7,3,8
3,2,5,12,7,12,9
7,16,5,5,2,2,11
4,13,8,15,7,1,13

Page 209
10,11,10,11,10,11,11
11,10,11,11,3,3,10,11
11,8,16,10,11,3,11
11,17,11,11,14,11,11
11,11,15,16,11,11,18
12,13,11,17,11,14,11

Page 210
11,8,11,4,1,11,8
1,11,6,1,10,11,2
11,6,2,11,1,2,11
11,2,11,9,7,11,7
7,11,2,11,9,9,11
11,7,11,2,7,11,9
5,2,7,11,11,7,7
11,9,11,5,7,11,7

Page 211
11,8,8,11,3,3,11
3,11,3,8,11,8,3
8,16,11,3,8,3,11

Page 212
11,3,11,8
11,11,4,11
7,7,11,3
11,8,11,7
4,11,7,3
11,4,8,11
3,11,11,4
8,9,3,4,9,5,8
9,8,6,3,7,8,9
3,9,9,2,8,9,3
3,3,8,9,8,3,9

Page 213
3,4,9,2,5,8,11
4,11,3,7,5,4,3
8,9,3,11,7,5,5
3,4,8,7,2,3,11
11,3,10,11,8,15,10
9,11,3,3,11,7,7
8,10,11,3,10,13,3
11,5,8,11,15,7,11

Page 214
8,8,12,11,8,8,11
12,3,14,8,11,12,4
8,8,6,11,4,12,3
11,3,12,4,8,11,16
11,14,8,8,8,3,13
16,5,12,11,13,11,8
3,12,8,13,10,6,5
14,5,8,10,3,8,11

Page 215
5,8,6,6,6,8,2
6,4,2,7,8,2,6
10,7,8,6,4,6,8
4,6,10,8,2,8,5
7,7,4,8
9,9,5,8
6,6,2,6
3,5,6,9
9,2,9,7
4,9,4,5
6,5,8,4

Page 216
6,10,4,9,6,5,8
6,7,7,4,6,10,3
5,4,8,8,7,6,5
7,6,11,4,5,8,14
16,6,9,11,5,5,6
7,8,2,4,12,6,11
6,11,6,8,18,4,6
3,7,5,10,5,2,6

Page 217
6,9,6,8,11,5,3
9,7,3,4,6,11,9
8,6,3,7,3,4,11
5,11,6,9,8,8,6
5,6,12,6
14,1,7,1
4,12,1,8
13,1,6,11
1,5,17,15
6,16,1,7
1,1,8,4

Page 218
8,10,4,7,3,6,10
7,5,10,8,6,7,7
10,4,3,5,7,5,10
6,10,6,6,7,3,8
7,12,14,6
8,16,4,10
14,8,12,8
6,10,5,4
12,7,6,14
16,6,6,5
8,14,12,10

Page 219
5,9,9,6,11,3,9
11,6,5,5,9,5,11
9,5,6,5,11,2,6
5,11,9,4,6,7,9
11,5,15,7,11,11,8
15,8,6,11,7,5,15
7,15,11,6,15,8,5
15,6,15,8,11,5,7

Page 220
11,14,5,12,6,16,10
6,12,8,11,14,5,12
10,5,12,6,8,10,16
11,8,6,11,16,14,6
14,10,5,14,6,12,11
11,8,10,11
5,4,5,2
2,6,11,6
10,8,8,5
6,2,6,11

Page 221
6,9,15,7,7,13,7
13,11,7,9,6,15,13
11,6,13,5,13,7,7
5,13,15,7,6,5,11
13,7,2,13
5,2,6,2
13,8,13,7
3,8,8,2
7,2,13,5
2,6,2,13
2,5,6,2

Page 222
13,0,4,7,5,6,6
7,7,6,9,8,13,2
6,13,4,6,5,0,8
6,7,6,13,4,6,7
7,13,15,7,8,6,13
7,15,6,7,13,8,6
15,7,8,13,7,7,15
6,13,15,8,15,7,7

Page 223
7,12,4,6,4,7,12
8,7,8,12,11,7,11
11,8,6,4,4,6,12
4,4,11,7,12,7,11
6,7,3,3,2,13,9
5,7,7,9,6,4,4
7,5,4,13,9,7,7
3,3,6,4,2,5,5

Page 224
8,15,7,6,7,15,8
15,6,5,7,15,4,8
7,6,8,8,5,7,15
7,8,4,15,6,7,7
15,8,9,2,12,8,15
7,12,7,7,15,9,4
12,8,5,8,7,7,2
2,4,7,15,2,7,8

Page 225
7,8,15,11,3,10,15
8,8,4,8,11,6,2
8,11,6,8,15,7,2
11,8,3,15,2,2,8
8,10,15,7,7,16,11
6,4,12,14,8,7,7
15,11,7,8,15,10,8
7,8,15,12,4,11,14

Page 226
11,3,18,6,12,15,11
0,5,11,11,8,8,13
3,17,11,2,1,18,8
16,8,2,3,14,11,0
8,11,5,11,6,11,11
6,5,11,3,11,8,3
11,3,11,8,11,11,6
8,11,6,11,5,3,11

Page 227
3,13,6,7,8,11,13
6,8,11,3,13,7,3
13,11,7,11,6,8,13
11,6,8,13,7,11,3
11,3,8,3,10,7,9
9,11,3,8,4,2,11
5,8,10,7,9,10,3
10,7,9,11,9,3,6

Page 228
11,8,14,2,2,3,16
12,11,2,6,2,11,8
3,2,2,11,2,10,12
2,8,8,2,14,3,11
8,13,3,5
15,9,11,8
7,11,17,13
11,5,11,11
3,15,11,3
9,8,7,11

Page 229
7,10,5,7,6,3,10
7,6,6,10,7,7,6
7,3,5,8,7,10,7
7,5,10,6,7,6,8
8,1,1,7
1,6,1,7
6,8,6,5
1,7,8,1
1,7,6,6
7,1,7,1
5,1,7,6

Page 230
6,2,6,7,2,5,2
2,8,2,2,2,7,7
5,2,7,2,6,8,2
2,6,5,2,8,7,2
7,9,7,7
5,8,8,7
5,6,6,3
7,2,6,5
6,8,7,6
4,5,7,1
6,6,8,7

Page 231
13,7,1,12,7,9,13
11,8,3,15,15,6,8
8,5,14,8,6,9,3
8,5,6,9,10,5,11
7,4,8,7,18,8,4
7,6,2,4,10,15,1
4,12,3,11,5,10,3
3,7,11,11,3,2,12

Page 232
9,9,4,13,3,7,5
11,9,10,2,11,12,5
0,6,5,13,8,4,5
14,4,8,12,6,2,5
15,6,6,11,8,7,8
2,10,5,7,7,12,4
7,6,6,3,4,2,8
11,14,2,14,8,8,10

Name _____

TRICK   Big Subtraction Shortcut

You know
$$\begin{array}{r} 6 \\ + 4 \\ \hline 10 \end{array}$$
(5 is in the Middle.)
and
$$\begin{array}{r} 4 \\ + 6 \\ \hline 10 \end{array}$$

Use this shortcut to learn
$$\begin{array}{r} 10 \\ - 4 \\ \hline 6 \end{array}$$
$$\begin{array}{r} 10 \\ - 6 \\ \hline 4 \end{array}$$

~~10~~   **Cut** the 10 in half.
$$\begin{array}{r} - 4 \\ \hline 6 \end{array}$$
5   (5+5=10)

4   5   6

4 goes with 6

~~10~~   **Cut** the 10 in half.
$$\begin{array}{r} - 6 \\ \hline 4 \end{array}$$
5   (5+5=10)

6   5   4

6 goes with 4

Practice **Big Subtraction Shortcut**. Mark **Shortcut** ~~10~~

~~10~~	5	10	10	10	5	10
− 4	+ 5	− 6	− 4	− 5	+ 5	− 6

4	10	5	10	6	10	10
+ 6	− 6	+ 5	− 6	+ 4	− 4	− 1

10	6	10	10	10	4	5
− 6	+ 4	− 4	− 1	− 4	+ 6	+ 5

10	10	6	10	4	10	10
− 4	− 6	+ 4	− 4	+ 6	− 6	− 4

Two Plus Two Is Not Five, Easy Methods To Learn Addition and Subtraction

Name _____

Practice **Big Subtraction Shortcut**, **Lots of 4s**, and **Count by 3s**.

10 − 4	8 + 4	9 − 6	10 − 6	4 + 8	10 − 6	12 − 8
6 + 3	10 − 4	12 − 4	9 − 3	10 − 4	4 + 8	3 + 6
9 − 3	12 − 8	10 − 6	3 + 6	12 − 4	12 − 8	10 − 4
10 − 6	9 − 6	8 + 4	10 − 4	6 + 3	10 − 6	12 − 4

Practice **Big Subtraction Shortcut**, **Number in the Middle**, and **Zero**.

10 − 6	5 + 7	8 + 6	3 − 3	3 + 5	10 − 4	4 + 6
0 + 8	7 + 5	10 − 6	10 − 4	7 − 0	6 + 8	5 + 7
1 − 1	10 − 6	0 + 4	6 + 4	4 − 0	10 − 4	9 + 7
8 + 6	7 − 7	10 − 4	5 + 3	9 + 0	1 + 0	10 − 6

Two Plus Two Is Not Five, Easy Methods To Learn Addition and Subtraction

Name _____

TRICK   Big Subtraction Shortcut

You know $\begin{array}{r} 7 \\ + 5 \\ \hline 12 \end{array}$ and $\begin{array}{r} 5 \\ + 7 \\ \hline 12 \end{array}$

(6 is in the Middle.)

Use this shortcut to learn $\begin{array}{r} 12 \\ - 5 \\ \hline 7 \end{array}$ $\begin{array}{r} 12 \\ - 7 \\ \hline 5 \end{array}$

$\begin{array}{r} \cancel{12} \\ - 5 \\ \hline 7 \end{array}$ Cut the 12 in half.   (6+6=12)

5 6 7

5 goes with 7

$\begin{array}{r} \cancel{12} \\ - 7 \\ \hline 5 \end{array}$ Cut the 12 in half.   (6+6=12)

7 6 5

7 goes with 5

Practice **Big Subtraction Shortcut**. Mark **Shortcut** ~~12~~ and ~~10~~

~~12~~ − 5	6 + 6	12 − 7	12 − 5	12 − 7	7 + 5	12 − 5
10 − 6	12 − 7	6 + 6	12 − 7	7 + 5	12 − 5	10 − 6
12 − 7	5 + 7	12 − 5	10 − 4	12 − 5	6 + 6	12 − 7
10 − 4	12 − 7	10 − 6	12 − 5	6 + 6	10 − 6	5 + 7

Name _____

Practice **Big Subtraction Shortcut**, **2 Ladder**, and **Number +1**.

12	8	9	12	2	10	1
− 7	+ 2	+ 1	− 5	+ 6	− 4	+ 5

6	10	12	10	4	12	10
+ 1	− 6	− 5	− 8	− 2	− 7	− 4

12	1	10	3	2	10	12
− 7	+ 4	− 2	+ 1	+ 8	− 6	− 7

10	8	7	10	1	6	6
− 4	− 6	+ 1	− 6	+ 2	− 2	+ 2

8	12	2	1	6	12	1
− 2	− 5	+ 4	+ 8	− 4	− 5	+ 7

Practice **Big Subtraction Shortcut**, **Straight Lines**, and **Curvy Numbers**.

12	4	8	10	13	11	12
− 5	+ 7	+ 5	− 4	− 5	− 7	− 5

3	7	10	12	11	5	8
+ 5	+ 4	− 6	− 7	− 4	+ 8	− 5

11	8	13	4	10	5	12
− 7	− 3	− 8	+ 7	− 4	+ 3	− 7

Two Plus Two Is Not Five, Easy Methods To Learn Addition and Subtraction

Name _____

Practice **Big Subtraction Shortcut** and **Lots of 4s**.

12	4	10	12	12	10	12
− 5	+ 8	− 4	− 4	− 8	− 6	− 7

10	12	12	10	8	12	10
− 6	− 7	− 4	− 4	+ 4	− 8	− 6

8	10	12	4	12	10	12
+ 4	− 4	− 5	+ 8	− 4	− 4	− 8

12	12	4	10	8	12	4
− 4	− 7	+ 8	− 6	+ 4	− 5	+ 8

Practice **Big Subtraction Shortcut** and **Looks Like Number in the Middle**.

10	9	12	5	10	6	12
− 4	− 7	− 7	− 3	− 8	− 4	− 5

8	12	7	12	10	5	10
− 6	− 5	− 5	− 7	− 6	− 3	− 4

9	7	10	6	4	12	10
− 7	− 5	− 6	− 4	− 2	− 7	− 8

6	10	9	8	12	10	5
− 4	− 4	− 7	− 6	− 5	− 6	− 3

Two Plus Two Is Not Five, Easy Methods To Learn Addition and Subtraction

Name _____

Practice **Big Subtraction Shortcut** and **Stretch**.

12	7	10	12	3	10	12
− 7	+ 3	− 7	− 5	+ 7	− 6	− 5

3	10	12	10	7	10	10
+ 7	− 4	− 7	− 6	+ 3	− 3	− 7

10	7	10	12	10	7	12
− 3	+ 3	− 3	− 7	− 4	+ 3	− 5

10	12	3	10	12	10	3
− 6	− 5	+ 7	− 4	− 7	− 7	+ 7

Practice **Big Subtraction Shortcut** and **Number Families**.

12−5= _____   10−4= _____   9−7= _____   7−2= _____

5+2= _____   7+2= _____   12−7= _____   2+7= _____

10−6= _____   7−5= _____   2+5= _____   12−5= _____

7+2= _____   10−4= _____   10−6= _____   9−2= _____

7−2= _____   12−7= _____   7−5= _____   12−5= _____

9−2= _____   10−6= _____   9−7= _____   2+7= _____

12−5= _____   5+2= _____   12−7= _____   10−4= _____

Name _____

TRICK   Big Subtraction Short**cut**

You know
$$\begin{array}{r} 8 \\ + 6 \\ \hline 14 \end{array}$$
and   (7 is in the Middle.)
$$\begin{array}{r} 6 \\ + 8 \\ \hline 14 \end{array}$$

Use this short**cut** to learn
$$\begin{array}{r} 14 \\ - 6 \\ \hline 8 \end{array}$$
$$\begin{array}{r} 14 \\ - 8 \\ \hline 6 \end{array}$$

$$\begin{array}{r} \cancel{14} \\ - 6 \\ \hline 8 \end{array}$$
7   **Cut** the 14 in half.   (7+7=14)
6 7 8
6 goes with 8

$$\begin{array}{r} \cancel{14} \\ - 8 \\ \hline 6 \end{array}$$
7   **Cut** the 14 in half.   (7+7=14)
8 7 6
8 goes with 6

Practice **Big Subtraction Short<u>cut</u>**. Mark **Shortcut** ~~14~~ ~~12~~ and ~~10~~

~~14~~	7	14	14	10	12	14
− 6	+ 7	− 8	− 6	− 6	− 7	− 8

6	14	12	10	14	5	10
+ 8	− 8	− 5	− 4	− 6	+ 5	− 6

12	10	14	6	12	14	7
− 7	− 6	− 6	+ 8	− 7	− 8	+ 7

14	8	12	14	10	12	10
− 8	+ 6	− 5	− 6	− 5	− 6	− 4

Two Plus Two Is Not Five, Easy Methods To Learn Addition and Subtraction   **193**

Name _____

Practice **Big Subtraction Shortcut** and **Doubles**.

14 − 6	10 − 4	5 + 5	6 + 6	12 − 7	6 − 3	10 − 6
7 + 7	16 − 8	12 − 5	8 − 4	14 − 7	10 − 5	14 − 8
3 + 3	12 − 7	4 + 4	12 − 6	2 + 2	14 − 6	4 − 2
14 − 8	8 + 8	10 − 6	18 − 9	1 + 1	12 − 5	10 − 4

Practice **Big Subtraction Shortcut** and **Double +1**.

12−5= _____   14−6= _____   10−6= _____   7+6= _____

3+4= _____   10−4= _____   8+7= _____   14−8= _____

12−7= _____   5+6= _____   14−6= _____   4+5= _____

10−6= _____   12−5= _____   6+7= _____   5+6= _____

14−8= _____   9+8= _____   12−7= _____   10−4= _____

8+7= _____   14−8= _____   6+5= _____   3+2= _____

5+4= _____   12−7= _____   7+8= _____   14−6= _____

Name _____

Practice **Big Subtraction Shortcut**, **Zero**, and **Right Next to Each Other**.

14 −8	3 −0	9 −8	12 −7	0 +3	10 −9	10 −4
6 −5	12 −5	14 −6	7 −6	4 −4	14 −8	12 −7
4 +0	10 −6	3 −2	12 −5	14 −6	5 −4	8 −7
14 −6	12 −7	1 −0	10 −6	12 −5	7 −7	14 −8

Practice **Big Subtraction Shortcut** and **Big Subtraction**.

10 −6	14 −8	17 −9	13 −4	12 −7	12 −3	14 −6
14 −8	11 −9	10 −4	18 −9	14 −5	15 −6	14 −9
12 −5	16 −9	14 −6	17 −8	12 −9	11 −2	10 −6
15 −9	13 −9	12 −7	14 −8	12 −5	10 −4	16 −7

Two Plus Two Is Not Five, Easy Methods To Learn Addition and Subtraction

Name _____

Cumulative Practice.

4 + 8	12 − 6	10 − 4	4 + 2	7 − 1	14 − 8	12 − 5
3 + 7	14 − 6	3 + 5	15 − 9	7 + 8	8 + 4	10 − 6
8 − 0	11 − 7	5 + 8	4 + 6	7 − 5	1 + 2	9 − 6
10 − 4	7 − 2	11 − 2	7 + 6	12 − 7	9 − 7	13 − 8
6 + 7	10 − 2	13 − 4	4 + 7	10 − 7	12 − 4	8 + 6
7 − 6	9 − 5	2 + 7	12 − 5	8 − 6	4 + 3	11 − 4
12 − 8	4 − 2	14 − 6	17 − 8	10 − 6	7 + 2	10 − 8
7 + 3	5 + 7	2 + 5	8 − 3	14 − 8	10 − 3	9 − 4

Two Plus Two Is Not Five, Easy Methods To Learn Addition and Subtraction

Name _____

TRICK Family Partners

You know   5   and   6   Learn   **11**   **11**
           + 6   + 5   − 5   − 6
           ―――   ―――   ―――   ―――
            11   11   6   5

What number is missing from the family?

   5 + _____ = 11   6 + _____ = 11

   5   11   6   6   11   5   11
  + 11   − 5   + 5   + 11   − 6   + 6   − 5
  ―――   ―――   ―――   ―――   ―――   ―――   ―――

   11   5   11   11   11   6   5
  − 6   + 6   −   − 6   − 5   + 5   + 11
  ―――   ―――   ―――   ―――   ―――   ―――   ―――
                          6

   11   6   11   11   5   11   6
  − 5   + 6   − 6   − 5   + 6   − 6   + 5
  ―――   ―――   ―――   ―――   ―――   ―――   ―――

Practice **Family Partners** and **Stretch**.

   11   7   11   10   10   11   3
  − 6   + 3   − 5   − 3   − 7   − 6   + 7
  ―――   ―――   ―――   ―――   ―――   ―――   ―――

   11   10   3   11   7   10   11
  − 5   − 7   + 7   − 6   + 3   − 3   − 5
  ―――   ―――   ―――   ―――   ―――   ―――   ―――

   3   10   11   7   11   11   10
  + 7   − 3   − 5   + 3   − 5   − 6   − 7
  ―――   ―――   ―――   ―――   ―――   ―――   ―――

Two Plus Two Is Not Five, Easy Methods To Learn Addition and Subtraction   **197**

Name _____

Practice **Number Family 5•6•11** and **Straight Lines**.

11 − 6	11 − 5	7 + 4	11 − 7	6 + 5	11 − 5	11 − 4

6 + 5	4 + 7	11 − 6	7 + 4	11 − 6	4 + 7	11 − 7

11 − 5	5 + 6	11 − 7	11 − 5	6 + 5	11 − 4	11 − 6

7 + 4	11 − 4	5 + 6	11 − 4	11 − 6	5 + 6	4 + 7

Practice **Number Family** and **Doubles** this way.

6+5= _____   11−6= _____   9+9= _____   10−5= _____

11−5= _____   6+6= _____   11−6= _____   7+7= _____

18−9= _____   4+4= _____   14−7= _____   5+6= _____

8+8= _____   11−6= _____   8−4= _____   6−3= _____

2+2= _____   11−5= _____   16−8= _____   5+5= _____

5+6= _____   1+1= _____   11−6= _____   6+5= _____

12−6= _____   5+6= _____   3+3= _____   11−5= _____

Two Plus Two Is Not Five, Easy Methods To Learn Addition and Subtraction

Name _____

Practice **Family Partners**, **Looks like Number in the Middle**, and **Magic 9**.

11 − 5	9 − 7	3 + 9	7 − 5	11 − 6	7 + 9	11 − 5
6 − 4	11 − 6	8 − 6	11 − 5	9 + 8	9 − 7	11 − 6
11 − 5	9 + 4	2 + 9	4 − 2	11 − 6	10 − 8	6 + 9
5 − 3	9 + 5	11 − 5	8 − 6	7 − 5	11 − 6	10 − 8

Practice **Number Families** and **Lots of 4s**.

5 + 6	8 + 4	11 − 5	7 − 5	12 − 8	4 + 8	9 − 7
9 − 4	11 − 5	6 + 5	4 + 5	9 − 2	12 − 4	11 − 6
8 + 4	12 − 8	11 − 6	12 − 4	7 + 2	5 + 2	9 − 5
11 − 6	9 − 7	5 + 4	7 − 2	4 + 8	11 − 5	7 − 5

Two Plus Two Is Not Five, Easy Methods To Learn Addition and Subtraction

Name _____

Practice **Number Family** and **Double +1**.

11 − 5	7 + 8	6 + 5	11 − 5	3 + 2	11 − 6	5 + 6
11 − 6	5 + 4	11 − 5	3 + 4	11 − 6	6 + 5	6 + 7
8 + 7	11 − 5	7 + 6	11 − 6	4 + 3	8 + 9	11 − 5

Cumulative Practice.

6 + 6	4 + 2	8 − 7	5 + 7	15 − 9	11 − 5	7 − 2
11 − 6	17 − 8	7 + 3	11 − 4	8 + 6	2 + 5	9 + 8
12 − 8	5 + 4	8 − 4	11 − 5	5 + 3	4 + 8	5 + 6
10 − 8	9 − 5	11 − 6	9 − 3	10 − 7	4 + 7	9 − 2
6 + 5	7 + 2	16 − 8	4 + 6	6 + 7	5 + 8	11 − 6

Two Plus Two Is Not Five, Easy Methods To Learn Addition and Subtraction

Name _____

TRICK Family Partners

You know $\begin{array}{r} 6 \\ +7 \\ \hline 13 \end{array}$ and $\begin{array}{r} 7 \\ +6 \\ \hline 13 \end{array}$ Learn $\begin{array}{r} 13 \\ -6 \\ \hline 7 \end{array}$ $\begin{array}{r} 13 \\ -7 \\ \hline 6 \end{array}$

What number is missing from the family?

$7 + \underline{\hspace{2cm}} = 13$ $6 + \underline{\hspace{2cm}} = 13$

$\begin{array}{r} 7 \\ + \\ \hline 13 \end{array}$ $\begin{array}{r} 13 \\ -7 \\ \hline \end{array}$ $\begin{array}{r} 6 \\ + \\ \hline 13 \end{array}$ $\begin{array}{r} 13 \\ -6 \\ \hline \end{array}$ $\begin{array}{r} 7 \\ +6 \\ \hline \end{array}$ $\begin{array}{r} 13 \\ -7 \\ \hline \end{array}$ $\begin{array}{r} 13 \\ -6 \\ \hline \end{array}$

$\begin{array}{r} 7 \\ +6 \\ \hline \end{array}$ $\begin{array}{r} 13 \\ -6 \\ \hline \end{array}$ $\begin{array}{r} 6 \\ +7 \\ \hline \end{array}$ $\begin{array}{r} 6 \\ + \\ \hline 13 \end{array}$ $\begin{array}{r} 13 \\ -6 \\ \hline \end{array}$ $\begin{array}{r} 6 \\ +6 \\ \hline \end{array}$ $\begin{array}{r} 13 \\ -7 \\ \hline \end{array}$

$\begin{array}{r} 13 \\ -6 \\ \hline \end{array}$ $\begin{array}{r} 7 \\ +6 \\ \hline \end{array}$ $\begin{array}{r} 13 \\ -7 \\ \hline \end{array}$ $\begin{array}{r} 13 \\ -6 \\ \hline \end{array}$ $\begin{array}{r} 7 \\ + \\ \hline 13 \end{array}$ $\begin{array}{r} 13 \\ -7 \\ \hline \end{array}$ $\begin{array}{r} 6 \\ +7 \\ \hline \end{array}$

Practice **Family Partners** and **Number Family 3•4•7** this way.

13−7= _____   4+3= _____   13−7= _____   7−4= _____

7−4= _____   13−6= _____   7−3= _____   13−6= _____

3+4= _____   4+3= _____   13−6= _____   7−3= _____

13−6= _____   7−3= _____   7−4= _____   13−7= _____

7−3= _____   13−7= _____   13−6= _____   3+4= _____

Two Plus Two Is Not Five, Easy Methods To Learn Addition and Subtraction

Name _____

Practice **Number Family 6•7•13** and **2 Ladder**.

6 + 7	8 + 2	13 − 7	6 + 2	6 − 4	7 + 6	13 − 6
8 − 2	13 − 6	7 + 6	10 − 2	6 + 7	13 − 7	10 − 8
13 − 6	2 + 6	4 + 2	13 − 7	8 − 6	2 + 8	7 + 6
2 + 4	10 − 8	13 − 7	6 + 7	6 − 2	13 − 6	4 − 2

Practice **Number Family** and **Big Subtraction**.

13 − 7	17 − 9	6 + 7	11 − 9	13 − 6	12 − 3	7 + 6
6 + 7	13 − 9	14 − 5	13 − 6	6 + 7	15 − 6	13 − 7
13 − 4	18 − 9	7 + 6	17 − 8	13 − 6	7 + 6	16 − 7
16 − 9	13 − 7	13 − 6	12 − 9	6 + 7	13 − 7	11 − 2

Two Plus Two Is Not Five, Easy Methods To Learn Addition and Subtraction

Name _____

Practice **Family Partners** and **Curvy Numbers**. (Circle) **Family Partners**.

(13) − 7	8 + 5	(13) − 6	5 + 8	13 − 5	13 − 7	8 − 5
5 + 8	13 − 6	13 − 8	8 − 3	13 − 6	5 + 3	13 − 7
13 − 6	8 − 5	5 + 8	13 − 5	3 + 5	13 − 6	13 − 8
8 + 5	13 − 7	13 − 5	8 − 3	13 − 8	13 − 7	8 + 5

Practice **Number Families** and **Backwards 1**.

13 − 6	9 − 1	3 + 2	6 − 1	5 − 3	7 + 6	2 + 7
9 − 7	4 − 1	13 − 6	9 − 2	6 + 7	5 − 2	3 − 1
13 − 7	2 + 3	7 + 2	13 − 7	9 − 7	7 − 1	13 − 6
2 + 7	5 − 2	6 + 7	10 − 1	13 − 7	9 − 2	5 − 3

Two Plus Two Is Not Five, Easy Methods To Learn Addition and Subtraction   **203**

Name _____

Practice **Family Partners**, **Lots of 4s**, and **Number +1**.

13 − 7	12 − 8	7 + 1	4 + 8	12 − 4	8 + 4	13 − 6
8 + 1	13 − 7	8 + 4	5 + 1	13 − 7	1 + 4	12 − 8
13 − 6	8 + 4	12 − 4	13 − 7	6 + 1	13 − 6	1 + 2
12 − 8	1 + 9	13 − 6	4 + 8	13 − 6	12 − 4	13 − 7

Practice **Number Family**, **Count by 3s**, and **Stretch**.

13 − 7	3 + 7	10 − 7	7 + 6	13 − 6	3 + 6	7 + 3
6 + 3	10 − 3	7 + 3	13 − 6	6 + 3	13 − 7	9 − 3
10 − 7	9 − 6	13 − 6	6 + 7	10 − 3	3 + 7	7 + 6
13 − 6	3 + 6	13 − 7	9 − 3	7 + 3	6 + 7	9 − 6

Two Plus Two Is Not Five, Easy Methods To Learn Addition and Subtraction

Name _____

TRICK Family Partners

You know $\begin{array}{r} 7 \\ +8 \\ \hline 15 \end{array}$ and $\begin{array}{r} 8 \\ +7 \\ \hline 15 \end{array}$ Learn $\begin{array}{r} \mathbf{15} \\ -7 \\ \hline 8 \end{array}$ $\begin{array}{r} \mathbf{15} \\ -8 \\ \hline 7 \end{array}$

These are also **Big Subtraction**.

Ask: What numbers are <u>bigger</u> or greater than **5**?

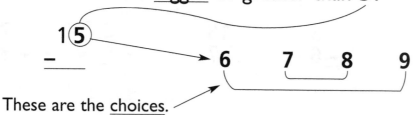

These are the <u>choices</u>.

$\begin{array}{cc} 7 & \text{goes with} & 8 \end{array}$

6 goes with 9

(You already know <u>Big Subtraction</u>: 15–6 and 15–9.)

Practice.

$\begin{array}{r} 7 \\ +8 \\ \hline \end{array}$ $\begin{array}{r} 7 \\ + \\ \hline 15 \end{array}$ $\begin{array}{r} 15 \\ -7 \\ \hline \end{array}$ $\begin{array}{r} 8 \\ +7 \\ \hline \end{array}$ $\begin{array}{r} 15 \\ -8 \\ \hline \end{array}$ $\begin{array}{r} 15 \\ -7 \\ \hline \end{array}$ $\begin{array}{r} 7 \\ +8 \\ \hline \end{array}$

$\begin{array}{r} 15 \\ -8 \\ \hline \end{array}$ $\begin{array}{r} 15 \\ -7 \\ \hline \end{array}$ $\begin{array}{r} 7 \\ +7 \\ \hline \end{array}$ $\begin{array}{r} 7 \\ + \\ \hline 15 \end{array}$ $\begin{array}{r} 15 \\ -8 \\ \hline \end{array}$ $\begin{array}{r} 8 \\ +8 \\ \hline \end{array}$ $\begin{array}{r} 15 \\ -7 \\ \hline \end{array}$

$\begin{array}{r} 5 \\ +5 \\ \hline \end{array}$ $\begin{array}{r} 15 \\ -8 \\ \hline \end{array}$ $\begin{array}{r} 15 \\ - \\ \hline 8 \end{array}$ $\begin{array}{r} 7 \\ +8 \\ \hline \end{array}$ $\begin{array}{r} 8 \\ -7 \\ \hline \end{array}$ $\begin{array}{r} 15 \\ -7 \\ \hline \end{array}$ $\begin{array}{r} 15 \\ -8 \\ \hline \end{array}$

Name _____

Practice **Number Family 7•8•15** and **Double +1**.

8 + 7	3 + 2	15 − 7	7 + 8	15 − 7	6 + 7	3 + 4
4 + 5	15 − 8	7 + 6	9 + 8	15 − 8	8 + 7	15 − 8
15 − 8	8 + 7	5 + 6	15 − 7	6 + 5	2 + 3	7 + 8
10 − 5	4 + 3	15 − 7	7 + 8	7 + 6	15 − 7	5 + 4

Practice **Number Family**, **Big Subtraction**, and **Doubles**.

15−7= _____	8+7= _____	15−9= _____	14−9= _____
7+7= _____	16−9= _____	17−8= _____	15−8= _____
10−5= _____	14−5= _____	7+8= _____	6+6= _____
11−2= _____	3+3= _____	13−9= _____	15−7= _____
6−3= _____	15−6= _____	8+8= _____	8+7= _____
15−8= _____	16−7= _____	18−9= _____	13−4= _____
12−9= _____	5+5= _____	7+8= _____	14−7= _____

Name _____

Practice **Family Partners**, **Lots of 4s**, and **Looks Like Number in the Middle**.

15 − 7	10 − 8	4 + 8	8 − 6	15 − 8	7 − 5	12 − 8
6 − 4	8 + 4	15 − 8	9 − 7	12 − 4	5 − 3	15 − 7
12 − 8	15 − 8	10 − 8	12 − 4	15 − 7	15 − 8	8 − 6
4 + 8	7 − 5	15 − 7	15 − 8	8 + 4	9 − 7	15 − 8

Practice **Family Partners**, **Magic 9**, and **Stretch**.

15−8= _____   4+9= _____   15−7= _____   10−3= _____

9+6= _____   3+7= _____   3+9= _____   15−8= _____

2+9= _____   9+9= _____   7+3= _____   7+9= _____

10−7= _____   15−7= _____   9+5= _____   3+7= _____

15−8= _____   7+3= _____   10−3= _____   15−7= _____

8+9= _____   10−7= _____   9+2= _____   15−8= _____

10−3= _____   9+4= _____   15−7= _____   10−7= _____

Two Plus Two Is Not Five, Easy Methods To Learn Addition and Subtraction   **207**

Name _____

Practice **Number Family**, **Curvy Numbers**, and **Count by 3s**.

15 − 7	6 + 3	7 + 8	5 + 8	9 − 3	13 − 5	15 − 8
9 − 6	8 + 7	8 − 3	3 + 6	8 − 5	8 + 7	3 + 5
13 − 8	9 − 3	15 − 8	13 − 5	6 + 3	8 − 3	9 − 6
8 + 5	15 − 7	8 − 5	13 − 8	15 − 7	9 − 3	7 + 8

Cumulative Practice.

7 + 5	12 − 4	3 + 7	15 − 8	5 + 2	9 − 6	15 − 7
7 − 4	8 − 6	14 − 9	3 + 9	14 − 7	4 + 8	13 − 4
10 − 3	8 + 8	9 − 4	13 − 8	7 − 5	9 − 7	7 + 4
11 − 7	5 + 8	15 − 7	9 + 6	15 − 8	4 − 3	7 + 6

Two Plus Two Is Not Five, Easy Methods To Learn Addition and Subtraction

Name _____

TRICK Family Pair

You know 8 + 2 is 10
So 8 + 3 is 11

Learn

$$\begin{array}{r} 8 \\ +3 \\ \hline 11 \end{array} \qquad \begin{array}{r} 3 \\ +8 \\ \hline 11 \end{array}$$

$$\begin{array}{r} 8 \\ +2 \\ \hline 10 \end{array} + \qquad 1\ \blacksquare \text{ more} = 11$$

Try.

$$\begin{array}{r} 2 \\ +8 \\ \hline \end{array} \qquad \begin{array}{r} 3 \\ +8 \\ \hline \end{array} \qquad \begin{array}{r} 8 \\ +2 \\ \hline \end{array} \qquad \begin{array}{r} 8 \\ +3 \\ \hline \end{array} \qquad \begin{array}{r} 2 \\ +8 \\ \hline \end{array} \qquad \begin{array}{r} 8 \\ +3 \\ \hline \end{array} \qquad \begin{array}{r} 3 \\ +8 \\ \hline \end{array}$$

$$\begin{array}{r} 8 \\ +3 \\ \hline \end{array} \qquad \begin{array}{r} 2 \\ +8 \\ \hline \end{array} \qquad \begin{array}{r} 8 \\ +3 \\ \hline \end{array} \qquad \begin{array}{r} 3 \\ +8 \\ \hline \end{array} \qquad \begin{array}{r} 8 \\ + \\ \hline 11 \end{array} \qquad \begin{array}{r} 2 \\ +8 \\ \hline \end{array} \qquad \begin{array}{r} 8 \\ +3 \\ \hline \end{array}$$

$$\begin{array}{r} 3 \\ +8 \\ \hline \end{array} \qquad \begin{array}{r} 3 \\ + \\ \hline 11 \end{array} \qquad \begin{array}{r} 8 \\ +8 \\ \hline \end{array} \qquad \begin{array}{r} 8 \\ +2 \\ \hline \end{array} \qquad \begin{array}{r} 8 \\ +3 \\ \hline \end{array} \qquad \begin{array}{r} 8 \\ + \\ \hline 11 \end{array} \qquad \begin{array}{r} 3 \\ +8 \\ \hline \end{array}$$

Practice **Family Pair** and **Magic 9**.

$$\begin{array}{r} 8 \\ +3 \\ \hline \end{array} \qquad \begin{array}{r} 8 \\ +9 \\ \hline \end{array} \qquad \begin{array}{r} 3 \\ +8 \\ \hline \end{array} \qquad \begin{array}{r} 8 \\ +3 \\ \hline \end{array} \qquad \begin{array}{r} 9 \\ +5 \\ \hline \end{array} \qquad \begin{array}{r} 2 \\ +9 \\ \hline \end{array} \qquad \begin{array}{r} 8 \\ +3 \\ \hline \end{array}$$

$$\begin{array}{r} 9 \\ +2 \\ \hline \end{array} \qquad \begin{array}{r} 8 \\ +3 \\ \hline \end{array} \qquad \begin{array}{r} 6 \\ +9 \\ \hline \end{array} \qquad \begin{array}{r} 9 \\ +7 \\ \hline \end{array} \qquad \begin{array}{r} 8 \\ +3 \\ \hline \end{array} \qquad \begin{array}{r} 3 \\ +8 \\ \hline \end{array} \qquad \begin{array}{r} 9 \\ +9 \\ \hline \end{array}$$

$$\begin{array}{r} 3 \\ +9 \\ \hline \end{array} \qquad \begin{array}{r} 9 \\ +4 \\ \hline \end{array} \qquad \begin{array}{r} 8 \\ +3 \\ \hline \end{array} \qquad \begin{array}{r} 9 \\ +8 \\ \hline \end{array} \qquad \begin{array}{r} 3 \\ +8 \\ \hline \end{array} \qquad \begin{array}{r} 5 \\ +9 \\ \hline \end{array} \qquad \begin{array}{r} 8 \\ +3 \\ \hline \end{array}$$

Two Plus Two Is Not Five, Easy Methods To Learn Addition and Subtraction **209**

Name _____

Practice **Family Pair**, **Right Next to Each Other**, and **2 Ladder**.

3 + 8	6 + 2	8 + 3	6 − 2	8 − 7	8 + 3	10 − 2
5 − 4	3 + 8	4 + 2	6 − 5	2 + 8	3 + 8	6 − 4
8 + 3	8 − 2	10 − 8	3 + 8	10 − 9	8 − 6	8 + 3

Practice **Family Pair** and **Number Families 2•5•7** and **2•7•9**.

8 + 3	9 − 7	3 + 8	2 + 7	5 + 2	8 + 3	2 + 5
9 − 2	3 + 8	7 − 5	8 + 3	2 + 7	7 + 2	3 + 8
8 + 3	5 + 2	8 + 3	7 − 5	9 − 2	3 + 8	2 + 7
7 − 2	9 − 7	2 + 5	3 + 8	8 + 3	9 − 2	5 + 2
3 + 8	7 + 2	3 + 8	7 − 2	2 + 5	8 + 3	9 − 2

Two Plus Two Is Not Five, Easy Methods To Learn Addition and Subtraction

Name _____

TRICK Family Partners

You know
$$\begin{array}{r} 8 \\ +\,3 \\ \hline 11 \end{array}$$
and
$$\begin{array}{r} 3 \\ +\,8 \\ \hline 11 \end{array}$$
Learn
$$\begin{array}{r} 11 \\ -\,8 \\ \hline 3 \end{array}$$
$$\begin{array}{r} 11 \\ -\,3 \\ \hline 8 \end{array}$$

These are also **Big Subtraction**.

Ask: What numbers are <u>bigger</u> or greater than **1**?

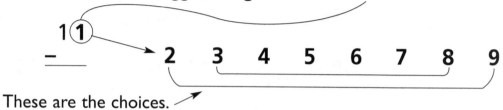

These are the <u>choices</u>.

3 goes with **8**

2 goes with 9 (You already know <u>Big Subtraction</u>: 11–2 and 11–9.)
3 goes with 8
4 goes with 7 (You already know <u>Straight Lines</u>: 11–7 and 11–4.)
5 goes with 6

Try.

$$\begin{array}{r} 8 \\ +\,3 \\ \hline \end{array}$$
$$\begin{array}{r} 3 \\ +\, \\ \hline 11 \end{array}$$
$$\begin{array}{r} 11 \\ -\,3 \\ \hline \end{array}$$
$$\begin{array}{r} 8 \\ +\,3 \\ \hline \end{array}$$
$$\begin{array}{r} 8 \\ +\, \\ \hline 11 \end{array}$$
$$\begin{array}{r} 11 \\ -\,8 \\ \hline \end{array}$$
$$\begin{array}{r} 3 \\ +\,8 \\ \hline \end{array}$$

$$\begin{array}{r} 11 \\ -\,8 \\ \hline \end{array}$$
$$\begin{array}{r} 8 \\ +\,3 \\ \hline \end{array}$$
$$\begin{array}{r} 8 \\ +\, \\ \hline 11 \end{array}$$
$$\begin{array}{r} 11 \\ -\,3 \\ \hline \end{array}$$
$$\begin{array}{r} 8 \\ +\,3 \\ \hline \end{array}$$
$$\begin{array}{r} 11 \\ -\,3 \\ \hline \end{array}$$
$$\begin{array}{r} 11 \\ -\,8 \\ \hline \end{array}$$

$$\begin{array}{r} 11 \\ -\,3 \\ \hline \end{array}$$
$$\begin{array}{r} 8 \\ +\,8 \\ \hline \end{array}$$
$$\begin{array}{r} 3 \\ +\,8 \\ \hline \end{array}$$
$$\begin{array}{r} 11 \\ -\,8 \\ \hline \end{array}$$
$$\begin{array}{r} 11 \\ -\,3 \\ \hline \end{array}$$
$$\begin{array}{r} 11 \\ -\,8 \\ \hline \end{array}$$
$$\begin{array}{r} 8 \\ +\,3 \\ \hline \end{array}$$

Two Plus Two Is Not Five, Easy Methods To Learn Addition and Subtraction

Name _____

Practice **Number Family 3•8•11** and **Straight Lines**.

3+8= _____	11–8= _____	7+4= _____	11–3= _____
4+7= _____	8+3= _____	11–7= _____	3+8= _____
11–4= _____	11–4= _____	4+7= _____	11–8= _____
8+3= _____	11–3= _____	7+4= _____	11–4= _____
11–7= _____	3+8= _____	11–4= _____	11–8= _____
7+4= _____	11–7= _____	11–3= _____	8+3= _____
11–8= _____	4+7= _____	3+8= _____	11–7= _____

Practice **Family Partners** and **Big Subtraction**.

11	16	11	13	12	14	11
– 3	– 7	– 8	– 9	– 3	– 9	– 3

13	11	15	11	16	11	18
– 4	– 3	– 9	– 8	– 9	– 3	– 9

11	17	14	11	11	15	11
– 8	– 8	– 5	– 9	– 3	– 6	– 8

12	11	11	11	17	11	14
– 9	– 8	– 3	– 2	– 9	– 8	– 5

Name _____

Practice **Number Families**.

11 − 8	7 − 3	4 + 5	5 − 3	9 − 4	11 − 3	8 + 3
9 − 5	3 + 8	7 − 4	4 + 3	2 + 3	7 − 3	11 − 8
11 − 3	5 + 4	5 − 2	8 + 3	3 + 4	9 − 4	3 + 2
7 − 4	9 − 5	11 − 3	4 + 3	5 − 3	11 − 8	3 + 8

Practice **Number Family**, **Stretch**, and **Double +1**.

8 + 3	11 − 8	3 + 7	5 + 6	11 − 3	8 + 7	7 + 3
4 + 5	3 + 8	10 − 7	11 − 8	8 + 3	10 − 3	4 + 3
11 − 3	7 + 3	8 + 3	10 − 7	3 + 7	6 + 7	11 − 8
6 + 5	3 + 2	11 − 3	3 + 8	7 + 8	10 − 3	3 + 8

Two Plus Two Is Not Five, Easy Methods To Learn Addition and Subtraction

Name _____

Practice **Number Family**, **Lots of 4s**, and **Doubles**.

11 − 3	16 − 8	8 + 4	3 + 8	12 − 4	4 + 4	8 + 3
4 + 8	11 − 8	7 + 7	11 − 3	8 + 3	8 + 4	12 − 8
11 − 3	12 − 4	12 − 6	3 + 8	12 − 8	6 + 6	11 − 8
3 + 8	6 − 3	4 + 8	12 − 8	11 − 3	8 + 3	8 + 8

Practice **Number Family**, **Curvy Numbers**, and **Number in the Middle**.

3 + 8	8 + 6	13 − 5	5 + 3	11 − 3	11 − 8	8 + 5
9 + 7	8 − 3	7 + 5	8 + 3	8 + 5	3 + 8	11 − 3
11 − 8	5 + 7	3 + 5	5 + 8	6 + 4	2 + 4	13 − 8
6 + 8	13 − 8	11 − 3	4 + 6	8 − 5	13 − 5	8 + 3

Two Plus Two Is Not Five, Easy Methods To Learn Addition and Subtraction

Name _____

Tiers 1, 2, 3, 4, 5, and 6 Review
Review **Big Subtraction Shortcut** and **2 Ladder**.

12 − 7	2 + 6	14 − 8	10 − 4	8 − 2	14 − 6	6 − 4
4 + 2	10 − 6	8 − 6	12 − 5	14 − 6	10 − 8	14 − 8
8 + 2	12 − 5	10 − 2	14 − 8	6 − 2	10 − 4	6 + 2
10 − 6	8 − 2	2 + 8	10 − 2	10 − 8	14 − 6	12 − 7

Review **Big Subtraction Shortcut** and **Big Subtraction**.

12−5= _____	16−9= _____	10−6= _____	14−6= _____
13−4= _____	15−6= _____	12−7= _____	17−9= _____
15−9= _____	10−4= _____	11−9= _____	14−8= _____
12−9= _____	12−7= _____	10−4= _____	16−7= _____
14−5= _____	11−9= _____	12−3= _____	12−5= _____
10−6= _____	17−8= _____	13−9= _____	14−9= _____
14−8= _____	12−7= _____	14−6= _____	10−6= _____

Two Plus Two Is Not Five, Easy Methods To Learn Addition and Subtraction

Name _____

Review **Big Subtraction Shortcut** and **Number +1**.

14 − 8	1 + 9	10 − 6	8 + 1	5 + 1	12 − 7	14 − 6
10 − 4	12 − 5	1 + 6	3 + 1	10 − 4	9 + 1	2 + 1
12 − 7	10 − 6	7 + 1	14 − 6	12 − 5	14 − 8	1 + 4

Review **Big Subtraction Shortcut**, **Number Family**, and **Doubles**.

12 − 5	3 + 3	5 + 6	10 − 6	11 − 6	14 − 6	7 + 7
8 + 8	10 − 4	18 − 9	6 + 5	12 − 7	10 − 5	11 − 5
14 − 7	14 − 6	1 + 1	8 − 4	6 + 6	14 − 8	6 + 5
11 − 5	5 + 6	10 − 4	16 − 8	9 + 9	10 − 6	12 − 6
6 − 3	12 − 5	11 − 6	5 + 5	12 − 7	4 − 2	14 − 8

Two Plus Two Is Not Five, Easy Methods To Learn Addition and Subtraction

Name _____

Tiers 1, 2, 3, 4, 5, and 6 Review
Review **Big Subtraction Shortcut**, **Number Family**, and **Count by 3s**.

10 −4	3 +6	9 −3	14 −6	8 +3	12 −7	9 −6
6 +3	12 −5	11 −8	10 −6	14 −8	3 +8	6 +3
11 −3	14 −8	9 −6	12 −5	11 −8	10 −6	3 +8
12 −7	8 +3	10 −4	3 +6	14 −6	11 −3	9 −3

Review **Big Subtraction Shortcut**, **Magic 9**, and **Right Next to Each Other**.

12−7= _____   14−8= _____   9+3= _____   10−4= _____

5+9= _____   9−8= _____   12−5= _____   5−4= _____

10−6= _____   3+9= _____   8−7= _____   14−6= _____

9+4= _____   10−9= _____   10−4= _____   9+2= _____

4−3= _____   12−7= _____   8+9= _____   6+9= _____

14−8= _____   9+7= _____   3−2= _____   12−5= _____

7−6= _____   6−5= _____   14−6= _____   10−6= _____

Two Plus Two Is Not Five, Easy Methods To Learn Addition and Subtraction

Name _____

Tiers 1, 2, 3, 4, 5, and 6 Review

Review **Big Subtraction Shortcut** and **Stretch**.

14 − 6	3 + 7	10 − 6	12 − 5	10 − 7	10 − 4	7 + 3
10 − 3	12 − 7	7 + 3	14 − 6	14 − 8	10 − 3	12 − 5
3 + 7	10 − 6	10 − 7	12 − 7	10 − 3	12 − 7	3 + 7
14 − 8	7 + 3	14 − 8	10 − 4	12 − 5	10 − 7	14 − 6

Review **Big Subtraction Shortcut** and **Number in the Middle**.

12−5= _____   5+7= _____   8+6= _____   14−8= _____

3+5= _____   7+9= _____   10−6= _____   4+6= _____

6+8= _____   14−6= _____   7+5= _____   5+3= _____

10−4= _____   6+4= _____   12−7= _____   10−6= _____

7+5= _____   12−5= _____   14−8= _____   6+8= _____

9+7= _____   2+4= _____   10−4= _____   12−7= _____

14−6= _____   8+6= _____   5+7= _____   6+4= _____

 Two Plus Two Is Not Five, Easy Methods To Learn Addition and Subtraction

Name _____

Tiers 1, 2, 3, 4, 5, and 6 Review
Review **Number Family 5•6•11** and **Big Subtraction**.

11 − 6	18 − 9	13 − 4	11 − 5	5 + 6	12 − 9	11 − 2
6 + 5	11 − 5	11 − 6	14 − 9	15 − 6	11 − 6	6 + 5
17 − 8	11 − 6	15 − 9	11 − 6	5 + 6	11 − 9	11 − 5
11 − 6	5 + 6	16 − 7	13 − 9	11 − 5	16 − 9	14 − 5

Review **Number Families**.

5 + 6	11 − 6	8 + 7	15 − 8	6 + 5	5 + 6	15 − 7
7 + 8	15 − 7	11 − 5	6 + 5	15 − 8	11 − 6	7 + 8
15 − 8	7 + 8	6 + 5	11 − 5	7 + 8	15 − 7	11 − 6
8 + 7	11 − 5	8 + 7	15 − 7	5 + 6	11 − 6	15 − 8

Two Plus Two Is Not Five, Easy Methods To Learn Addition and Subtraction **219**

Name _____

Tiers 1, 2, 3, 4, 5, and 6 Review

Review **Number Family** and **Number in the Middle**.

6 + 5	8 + 6	11 − 6	7 + 5	2 + 4	9 + 7	4 + 6
11 − 5	5 + 7	3 + 5	5 + 6	6 + 8	11 − 6	5 + 7
6 + 4	11 − 6	7 + 5	11 − 5	5 + 3	6 + 4	7 + 9
5 + 6	5 + 3	11 − 5	6 + 5	7 + 9	8 + 6	11 − 5
8 + 6	4 + 6	11 − 6	6 + 8	11 − 5	5 + 7	6 + 5

Review **Number Family** and **2 Ladder**.

6+5= _____   10−2= _____   2+8= _____   5+6= _____

11−6= _____   6−2= _____   11−6= _____   8−6= _____

6−4= _____   11−5= _____   5+6= _____   11−5= _____

8+2= _____   6+2= _____   2+6= _____   11−6= _____

11−5= _____   10−8= _____   8−2= _____   6+5= _____

Two Plus Two Is Not Five, Easy Methods To Learn Addition and Subtraction

Name _____

Tiers 1, 2, 3, 4, 5, and 6 Review
Review **Number Family 6•7•13** and **Double +1**.

13	5	8	13	3	6	13
− 7	+ 4	+ 7	− 6	+ 4	+ 7	− 6

7	5	13	4	13	7	7
+ 6	+ 6	− 6	+ 5	− 7	+ 8	+ 6

6	13	6	3	6	13	4
+ 5	− 7	+ 7	+ 2	+ 7	− 6	+ 3

3	7	8	13	13	2	5
+ 2	+ 6	+ 7	− 6	− 7	+ 3	+ 6

Review **Number Family**, **Looks Like Number in the Middle**, and **Curvy Numbers**.

6+7= _____   13−6= _____   5−3= _____   8+5= _____

13−8= _____   7−5= _____   13−7= _____   9−7= _____

7+6= _____   3+5= _____   5+8= _____   13−6= _____

8−5= _____   13−5= _____   5+3= _____   8−6= _____

13−6= _____   10−8= _____   7+6= _____   13−8= _____

8−6= _____   13−7= _____   9−7= _____   6+7= _____

6−4= _____   8−3= _____   13−7= _____   7−5= _____

Two Plus Two Is Not Five, Easy Methods To Learn Addition and Subtraction   **221**

Name _____

Tiers 1, 2, 3, 4, 5, and 6 Review
Review **Number Family**, **Zero**, and **Big Subtraction Shortcut**.

7 + 6	3 − 3	10 − 6	12 − 5	5 + 0	13 − 7	10 − 4
13 − 6	7 + 0	14 − 8	9 − 0	14 − 6	6 + 7	0 + 2
10 − 4	7 + 6	4 − 0	13 − 7	12 − 7	9 − 9	14 − 6
14 − 8	13 − 6	0 + 6	6 + 7	10 − 6	13 − 7	12 − 5

Review **Number Families**.

13 − 6	6 + 7	7 + 8	15 − 8	15 − 7	13 − 7	7 + 6
15 − 8	8 + 7	13 − 7	13 − 6	6 + 7	15 − 7	13 − 7
7 + 8	13 − 6	15 − 7	6 + 7	15 − 8	13 − 6	8 + 7
13 − 7	7 + 6	8 + 7	15 − 7	7 + 8	15 − 8	13 − 6

Two Plus Two Is Not Five, Easy Methods To Learn Addition and Subtraction

Name _____

Tiers 1, 2, 3, 4, 5, and 6 Review
Review **Family Partners**, **Lots of 4s**, and **Straight Lines**.

13 − 6	4 + 8	11 − 7	13 − 7	12 − 8	11 − 4	8 + 4
12 − 4	11 − 4	12 − 4	8 + 4	4 + 7	13 − 6	7 + 4
4 + 7	12 − 4	13 − 7	12 − 8	11 − 7	13 − 7	4 + 8
12 − 8	11 − 7	7 + 4	13 − 6	8 + 4	11 − 4	4 + 7

Review **Number Families**.

13 − 7	3 + 4	7 − 4	5 − 2	5 − 3	7 + 6	4 + 5
9 − 4	13 − 6	4 + 3	5 + 4	13 − 7	9 − 5	7 − 3
13 − 6	3 + 2	9 − 5	6 + 7	5 + 4	3 + 4	13 − 6
5 − 2	7 − 4	13 − 7	7 − 3	5 − 3	9 − 4	2 + 3

Two Plus Two Is Not Five, Easy Methods To Learn Addition and Subtraction **223**

Name _____

Tiers 1, 2, 3, 4, 5, and 6 Review
Review **Number Family 7•8•15** and **Big Subtraction Shortcut**.

15 − 7	8 + 7	12 − 5	10 − 4	15 − 8	7 + 8	14 − 6
7 + 8	14 − 8	12 − 7	15 − 8	8 + 7	10 − 6	15 − 7
12 − 5	10 − 4	15 − 7	14 − 6	12 − 7	15 − 8	7 + 8
15 − 8	15 − 7	10 − 6	8 + 7	14 − 8	12 − 5	15 − 8

Review **Number Families** and **Lots of 4s**.

8 + 7	12 − 4	2 + 7	7 − 5	4 + 8	15 − 7	7 + 8
5 + 2	8 + 4	15 − 8	9 − 2	7 + 8	7 + 2	12 − 8
4 + 8	15 − 7	7 − 2	12 − 4	2 + 5	15 − 8	9 − 7
7 − 5	12 − 8	15 − 8	8 + 7	9 − 7	5 + 2	15 − 7

 Two Plus Two Is Not Five, Easy Methods To Learn Addition and Subtraction

Name _____

Tiers 1, 2, 3, 4, 5, and 6 Review
Review **Number Families** and **2 Ladder**.

15 − 8	6 + 2	7 + 8	3 + 8	11 − 8	8 + 2	8 + 7
15 − 7	11 − 3	6 − 2	15 − 7	8 + 3	2 + 4	10 − 8
11 − 3	3 + 8	8 − 2	2 + 6	7 + 8	15 − 8	6 − 4
8 + 3	10 − 2	11 − 8	8 + 7	4 − 2	8 − 6	15 − 7

Review **Number Family**, **Straight Lines**, and **Number in the Middle**.

15 − 7	6 + 4	7 + 8	15 − 8	11 − 4	7 + 9	4 + 7
4 + 2	11 − 7	7 + 5	8 + 6	3 + 5	15 − 8	11 − 4
8 + 7	7 + 4	11 − 4	15 − 7	7 + 8	4 + 6	15 − 7
15 − 8	5 + 3	8 + 7	5 + 7	11 − 7	4 + 7	6 + 8

Name _____

Tiers 1, 2, 3, 4, 5, and 6 Review
Review **Number Family 3•8•11**, **Magic 9**, and **Zero**.

3 + 8	11 − 8	9 + 9	6 − 0	3 + 9	9 + 6	8 + 3
6 − 6	0 + 5	9 + 2	8 + 3	11 − 3	8 + 0	4 + 9
11 − 8	9 + 8	3 + 8	2 − 0	0 + 1	9 + 9	11 − 3
7 + 9	11 − 3	2 + 0	11 − 8	9 + 5	3 + 8	2 − 2

Review **Number Families**.

11 − 3	3 + 8	11 − 6	5 + 6	11 − 5	8 + 3	6 + 5
11 − 5	11 − 6	8 + 3	11 − 8	5 + 6	11 − 3	11 − 8
3 + 8	11 − 8	5 + 6	11 − 3	3 + 8	6 + 5	11 − 5
11 − 3	6 + 5	11 − 5	3 + 8	11 − 6	11 − 8	8 + 3

Two Plus Two Is Not Five, Easy Methods To Learn Addition and Subtraction

Name _____

Tiers 1, 2, 3, 4, 5, and 6 Review
Review **Number Families**.

11 − 8	7 + 6	13 − 7	13 − 6	11 − 3	3 + 8	7 + 6
13 − 7	11 − 3	8 + 3	11 − 8	6 + 7	13 − 6	11 − 8
6 + 7	3 + 8	13 − 6	8 + 3	13 − 7	11 − 3	6 + 7
8 + 3	13 − 7	11 − 3	7 + 6	13 − 6	3 + 8	11 − 8

Review **Number Family**, **Big Subtraction**, and **Stretch**.

8 + 3	11 − 8	17 − 9	12 − 9	7 + 3	10 − 3	14 − 5
11 − 2	3 + 8	10 − 7	11 − 3	13 − 9	11 − 9	8 + 3
14 − 9	11 − 3	3 + 7	10 − 3	16 − 7	3 + 7	11 − 8
7 + 3	16 − 9	15 − 6	3 + 8	13 − 4	10 − 7	15 − 9

Two Plus Two Is Not Five, Easy Methods To Learn Addition and Subtraction **227**

Name _____

Tiers 1, 2, 3, 4, 5, and 6 Review

Review **Number Family**, **Looks Like Number in the Middle**, and **Number in the Middle**.

3 + 8	11 − 3	6 + 8	5 − 3	10 − 8	11 − 8	7 + 9
5 + 7	8 + 3	7 − 5	4 + 2	8 − 6	3 + 8	11 − 3
11 − 8	9 − 7	8 − 6	8 + 3	6 − 4	6 + 4	7 + 5
10 − 8	3 + 5	11 − 3	7 − 5	8 + 6	11 − 8	8 + 3

Review **Number Family** and **Double +1**.

11−3= _____	6+7= _____	11−8= _____	2+3= _____
7+8= _____	4+5= _____	3+8= _____	11−3= _____
4+3= _____	8+3= _____	8+9= _____	7+6= _____
8+3= _____	3+2= _____	6+5= _____	3+8= _____
11−8= _____	8+7= _____	8+3= _____	11−8= _____
5+4= _____	11−3= _____	3+4= _____	5+6= _____

Two Plus Two Is Not Five, Easy Methods To Learn Addition and Subtraction

Name _____

Tiers 1, 2, 3, 4, 5, and 6 Review
Review **Family Partners** and **Stretch**.

| 13
− 6 | 7
+ 3 | 11
− 6 | 15
− 8 | 11
− 5 | 10
− 7 | 3
+ 7 |

| 10
− 3 | 11
− 5 | 13
− 7 | 3
+ 7 | 10
− 3 | 15
− 8 | 13
− 7 |

| 13
− 6 | 10
− 7 | 11
− 6 | 15
− 7 | 15
− 8 | 7
+ 3 | 13
− 6 |

| 15
− 8 | 11
− 6 | 3
+ 7 | 13
− 7 | 10
− 3 | 11
− 5 | 15
− 7 |

Review **Family Partners** and **Right Next to Each Other**.

15−7= _____   8−7= _____   5−4= _____   13−6= _____

9−8= _____   13−7= _____   4−3= _____   15−8= _____

11−5= _____   15−7= _____   13−7= _____   11−6= _____

6−5= _____   13−6= _____   15−7= _____   7−6= _____

3−2= _____   15−8= _____   11−5= _____   13−7= _____

15−8= _____   5−4= _____   13−6= _____   9−8= _____

11−6= _____   10−9= _____   15−8= _____   11−5= _____

Two Plus Two Is Not Five, Easy Methods To Learn Addition and Subtraction

Name _____

Tiers 1, 2, 3, 4, 5, and 6 Review
Review **Family Partners** and **Looks Like Number in the Middle**.

13 − 7	8 − 6	11 − 5	15 − 8	7 − 5	11 − 6	9 − 7
7 − 5	15 − 7	10 − 8	5 − 3	6 − 4	13 − 6	15 − 8
11 − 6	9 − 7	13 − 6	8 − 6	11 − 5	15 − 7	6 − 4
5 − 3	13 − 7	11 − 6	9 − 7	15 − 7	15 − 8	10 − 8

Review **Family Partners** and **Backwards 1**.

13−6= _____   10−1= _____   15−8= _____   13−6= _____

11−6= _____   15−7= _____   9−1= _____   15−8= _____

6−1= _____   11−5= _____   13−7= _____   4−1= _____

15−8= _____   3−1= _____   11−5= _____   11−6= _____

13−7= _____   15−7= _____   8−1= _____   13−7= _____

5−1= _____   11−6= _____   13−6= _____   2−1= _____

11−5= _____   7−1= _____   15−7= _____   13−6= _____

Name _____

End of Book Review
Review all math tricks.

7 + 6	12 − 5	5 − 4	4 + 8	13 − 6	2 + 7	8 + 5
4 + 7	14 − 6	12 − 9	8 + 7	6 + 9	10 − 4	15 − 7
11 − 3	11 − 6	6 + 8	16 − 8	11 − 5	16 − 7	5 − 2
6 + 2	13 − 8	14 − 8	3 + 6	6 + 4	5 − 0	8 + 3
9 − 2	10 − 6	5 + 3	15 − 8	9 + 9	12 − 4	8 − 4
5 + 2	13 − 7	8 − 6	11 − 7	7 + 3	7 + 8	2 − 1
12 − 8	7 + 5	7 − 4	3 + 8	12 − 7	1 + 9	8 − 5
9 − 6	10 − 3	6 + 5	9 + 2	11 − 8	6 − 4	8 + 4

Two Plus Two Is Not Five, Easy Methods To Learn Addition and Subtraction **231**

Name _____

End of Book Review
Review all math tricks.

4 + 5	12 − 3	10 − 6	4 + 9	10 − 7	15 − 8	12 − 7
3 + 8	18 − 9	2 + 8	11 − 9	5 + 6	8 + 4	10 − 5
7 − 7	13 − 7	7 − 2	6 + 7	14 − 6	2 + 2	11 − 6
7 + 7	12 − 8	11 − 3	5 + 7	14 − 8	9 − 7	4 + 1
8 + 7	9 − 3	15 − 9	7 + 4	13 − 5	11 − 4	15 − 7
3 − 1	7 + 3	7 − 2	10 − 3	13 − 6	4 + 8	7 − 3
12 − 5	10 − 4	8 − 2	11 − 8	9 − 5	7 − 5	12 − 4
8 + 3	8 + 6	10 − 8	9 + 5	12 − 4	11 − 3	3 + 7

Congratulations

to _____

date _____

for Mastery
of Addition and
Subtraction Math Facts

Two Plus Two Is Not Five, Easy Methods To Learn Addition and Subtraction

Record-Keeping Checklist

Notes	Page	Trick Name	Facts in Order of Introduction
Tier 1			
_____	1	Number +1	1+1 1+2 1+3 1+4 1+5 1+6 1+7 1+8 1+9 2+1 3+1 4+1 5+1 6+1 7+1 8+1 9+1
_____	3	Doubles	2+2 5+5
_____	5	Backwards 1	2−1 3−1 4−1 5−1 6−1 7−1 8−1 9−1 10−1
_____	8	Doubles	3+3
_____	10	Zero	Number+0 0+Number
_____	12	Doubles	4+4 4−2 10−5
_____	17	Right Next to Each Other	3−2 4−3 5−4 6−5 7−6 8−7 9−8 10−9
_____	20	Doubles	6−3 8−4
_____	22	2 Ladder	2+4 4+2 2+6 6+2 2+8 8+2
Tier 2			
_____	25	Double +1	2+3 3+2 3+4 4+3
_____	31	Zero	9−9 8−8 7−7 6−6 5−5 4−4 3−3 2−2 1−1
_____	33	Doubles	6+6 12−6 7+7 14−7
_____	39	Zero	Number−0
_____	41	Number in the Middle	3+5 5+3 4+6 6+4
_____	45	Magic 9	9+2 2+9 9+3 3+9 9+4 4+9 9+5 5+9 9+6 6+9 9+7 7+9 9+8 8+9 9+9
Tier 3			
_____	57	Count by 3s	3+6 6+3 9−3 9−6
_____	61	Doubles	8+8 16−8 18−9
_____	65	Family Partners	5−2 5−3
_____	69	2 Ladder	6−2 8−2 10−2
_____	73	Double +1	4+5 5+4
_____	77	Family Partners	7−3 7−4
_____	81	Curvy Numbers	8+5 5+8 8−3 8−5 13−5 13−8
Tier 4			
_____	97	Straight Lines	4+7 7+4 11−4 11−7
_____	101	Family Partners	9−4 9−5
_____	105	Number in the Middle	5+7 7+5 6+8 8+6
_____	109	Big Subtraction	17−8 17−9 16−7 16−9 15−6 15−9 14−5 14−9 13−4 13−9 12−3 12−9 11−2 11−9
Tier 5			
_____	135	2 Ladder	6−4 8−6 10−8
_____	139	Double +1	5+6 6+5 6+7 7+6 7+8 8+7
_____	147	Family	2+7 7+2 9−2 9−7
_____	153	Lots of 4s	4+8 8+4 12−4 12−8
_____	159	Family	2+5 5+2 7−2 7−5
_____	165	Stretch	3+7 7+3 10−3 10−7
Tier 6			
_____	187	Big Subtraction Shortcut	10−4 10−6 12−5 12−7 14−6 14−8
_____	197	Family Partners	11−5 11−6 13−6 13−7 15−7 15−8
_____	209	Family	3+8 8+3 11−3 11−8

Name _____   Baseline Date _____

Math Facts Baseline Recorder

Addition and Subtraction

Name _____

Baseline Date _____   Addition Facts: +_____ / 81

Circle KNOWN facts.   Check KNOWN concepts of Zero.

81 Addition Facts

Concepts of Zero: (Number + Zero) _____   (Zero + Number) _____

1+1, 1+2, 2+1, 3+1, 1+3, 2+2, 3+2, 2+3, 4+1, 1+4, 1+5, 5+1,

2+4, 4+2, 3+3, 1+6, 6+1, 2+5, 5+2, 3+4, 4+3, 1+7, 7+1, 2+6, 6+2,

3+5, 5+3, 4+4, 1+8, 8+1, 2+7, 7+2, 3+6, 6+3, 4+5, 5+4, 1+9, 9+1,

2+8, 8+2, 3+7, 7+3, 4+6, 6+4, 5+5, 2+9, 9+2, 3+8, 8+3, 4+7, 7+4,

5+6, 6+5, 3+9, 9+3, 4+8, 8+4, 5+7, 7+5, 6+6, 4+9, 9+4, 5+8, 8+5,

6+7, 7+6, 5+9, 9+5, 6+8, 8+6, 7+7, 6+9, 9+6, 7+8, 8+7, 7+9, 9+7,

8+8, 8+9, 9+8,   9+9

Baseline Date _____   Subtraction Facts: +_____ / 81

Circle KNOWN facts.   Check KNOWN concepts of Zero.

81 Subtraction Facts

Concepts of Zero: (Number – Number) _____   (Number – Zero) _____

2–1, 3–1, 3–2, 4–1, 4–2, 4–3, 5–1, 5–2, 5–3, 5–4, 6–1, 6–2, 6–3,

6–4, 6–5, 7–1, 7–2, 7–3, 7–4, 7–5, 7–6, 8–1, 8–2, 8–3, 8–4, 8–5,

8–6, 8–7, 9–1, 9–2, 9–3, 9–4, 9–5, 9–6, 9–7, 9–8, 10–1, 10–2, 10–3,

10–4, 10–5, 10–6, 10–7, 10–8, 10–9, 11–2, 11–3, 11–4, 11–5, 11–6, 11–7, 11–8,

11–9, 12–3, 12–4, 12–5, 12–6, 12–7, 12–8, 12–9, 13–4, 13–5, 13–6, 13–7, 13–8,

13–9, 14–5, 14–6, 14–7, 14–8, 14–9, 15–6, 15–7, 15–8, 15–9, 16–7, 16–8, 16–9,

17–8, 17–9, 18–9

Two Plus Two Is Not Five, Easy Methods To Learn Addition and Subtraction   **235**

Index of Math Tricks

Answers are provided on the reverse side of the Tier Instructions and Information pages.

Backwards 1, Tier 1: 5-7, 9, 11-12, 15, 18, 23 Tier 2: 28, 32, 36, 39, 43, 47, 53, Tier 3: 57, 64, 66, 74, 79, 83, 89, 91 Tier 4: 99, 110, 129 Tier 5: 142, 150, 162, 165, 176, 182, Tier 6: 203, 230

Big Subtraction, Tier 4: 109-123, 126, 128, 131, 132 Tier 5: 137, 142, 148, 157, 159, 169, 172, 174, 180, 182 Tier 6: 195, 202, 206, 212, 215, 219, 227

Big Subtraction Shortcut, Tier 6: 187-195, 215-218, 222, 224

Count by 3s, Tier 3: 57-60, 85-86, 91 Tier 4: 98, 106, 112, 130 Tier 5: 136, 145, 150, 155, 161, 169, 181 Tier 6: 188, 204, 208, 217

Curvy Numbers, Tier 3: 81-85, 88, 93-94 Tier 4: 103, 108, 112, 119, 126, 130, 131 Tier 5: 138, 145, 152, 156, 162, 166, 172, 184 Tier 6: 190, 203, 208, 214, 221

Double +1, Tier 2: 25-29, 49, 52, 54 Tier 3: 73-75, 86, 89, 92, 94 Tier 4: 108, 114, 119, 125, 131 Tier 5: 139-146, 175-176, 178-179, 181 Tier 6: 194, 200, 206, 213, 221, 228

Doubles, Tier 1: 3-4, 6, 8-10, 12-15, 19-20, 23 Tier 2: 33-37, 50-51, 54 Tier 3: 61-64, 85, 87, 90-93 Tier 4: 98, 115, 121, 127 Tier 5: 143, 147, 154, 162, 166, 173 Tier 6: 194, 198, 206, 214, 216

Families
2•3•5 Tier 3: 65-68, 86-90, 94 Tier 4: 99, 108, 117, 128 Tier 5: 138, 168 Tier 6: 203, 213, 223
3•4•7 Tier 3: 77-80, 86-90, 94 Tier 4: 102, 107, 117, 128 Tier 5: 138, 168, Tier 6: 201, 213, 223
4•5•9 Tier 4: 101-103, 127-128, 130-131 Tier 5: 138, 144, 151, 163, 167, 182-183 Tier 6: 199, 213, 223
2•7•9 Tier 5: 147-152, 177-178, 182-183 Tier 6: 192, 199, 203, 210, 224
2•5•7 Tier 5: 159-163, 181-183 Tier 6: 192, 199, 210, 224
5•6•11 Tier 6: 197-200, 216, 219-220, 226, 229-230

6•7•13 Tier 6: 201-204, 221-223, 227, 229-230
7•8•15 Tier 6: 205-208, 219, 222, 224-225, 229-230
3•8•11 Tier 6: 209-214, 217, 225-228

Looks Like Number in the Middle, Tier 3: 65 Tier 5: 135, 149, 161, 171-172, 176-177, 180, 183 Tier 6: 191, 199, 207, 221, 228, 230

Lots of 4s, Tier 5: 153-157, 174, 177, 179-180, 182, 184 Tier 6: 188, 191, 199, 204, 207, 214, 223-224

Magic 9, Tier 2: 45-47, 49-51, 53-54 Tier 3: 59, 66, 71, 74, 79, 83, 86, 90 Tier 4: 99, 103, 107, 123, 129 Tier 5: 136, 140, 149, 160, 168, 175 Tier 6: 199, 207, 209, 217, 226

Number in the Middle, Tier 2: 41-44, 49, 51-52, 54 Tier 3: 59, 62, 67, 72, 75, 78, 84, 92 Tier 4: 105-108, 127, 129-130, 132 Tier 5: 137, 145, 148, 156, 163, 169, 171 Tier 6: 188, 214, 218, 220, 225, 228

Number +1, Tier 1: 1-4, 6-7, 9, 11, 15, 18, 23 Tier 2: 26, 28, 37, 42, 46 Tier 3: 57, 64, 67, 74, 89, 94 Tier 4: 99, 103, 119 Tier 5: 142, 160, 165, 172 Tier 6: 190, 204, 216

Right Next to Each Other, Tier 1: 17-20, 24 Tier 2: 28, 36, 40, 43, 47 Tier 3: 58, 66, 72, 75, 79, 82, 87-88, Tier 4: 97, 112, 129 Tier 5: 144, 154, 161, 166, 172 Tier 6: 195, 210, 217, 229

Straight Lines, Tier 4: 97-100, 125-126, 128, 130, 132 Tier 5: 140, 145, 151, 157, 160, 166, 171, 179, 183 Tier 6: 190, 198, 212, 223, 225

Stretch, Tier 5: 165-170, 173, 175, 180, 183-184 Tier 6: 192, 197, 204, 207, 213, 218, 227, 229

2 Ladder, Tier 1: 22-24 Tier 2: 26, 29, 32, 34, 37, 40, 52-53 Tier 3: 69-72, 87, 90-93 Tier 4: 102, 107, 110, 123, 125, 129 Tier 5: 135-138, 173-174, 176, 178-179, 181 Tier 6: 190, 202, 210, 215, 220, 225

Zero, Tier 1: 10-11, 13, 15, 19 Tier 2: 31-32, 39-40, 50, 52 Tier 3: 58, 62, 67, 71, 75, 78, 82, 87, 91 Tier 4: 99, 117, 128 Tier 5: 144, 150, 163, 168, 180 Tier 6: 188, 195, 222, 226